AND THE
SNOW
OF THE
CENTURY

Takahiko Mukoyama
Tetsuo Takashima
with studio ET CETERA

GENTOSHA

Miracles come in strange ways.

— *words from a fortune cookie*

"...Yeah, I know you'd rather be with your family or friends than listening to a DJ on Christmas night — but I'll try my best to keep you from getting lonely.

"There's a huge cold front coming in directly over the Spyglass area. It looks like the weather is going to be really wild tonight. — Heck, this might even be the biggest snowstorm of the century!

"So shut your garage doors and buy plenty of food. It's going to be a long night."

"Meanwhile, here's a good Christmas number... This one's just for you."

"Oh, darling..."

"Why was I so young...
So young and so hopeful..."

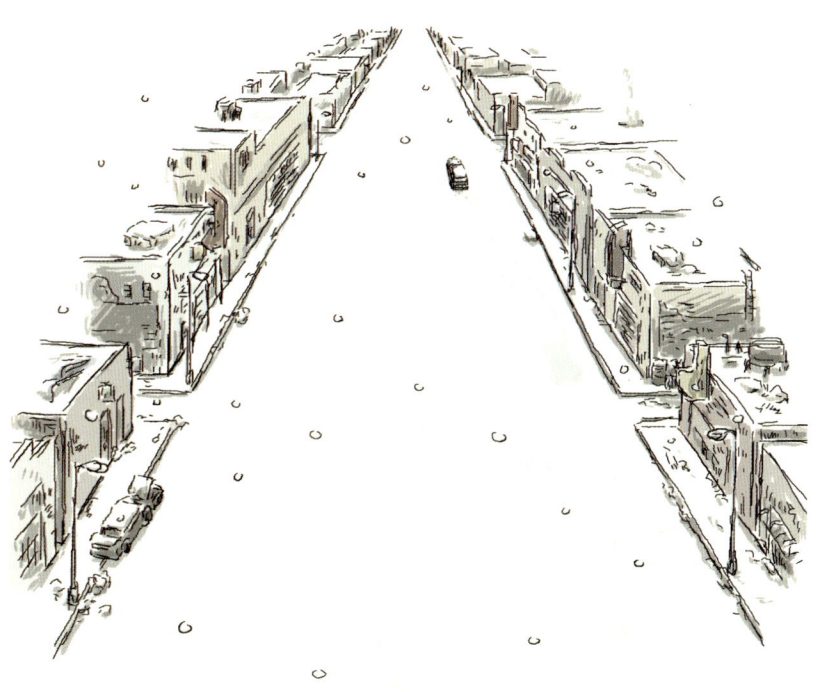

"Why do my memories come back to me..."

"Oooohhh..."

"On Christmas Daaay..."

    The street corner was a bus stop but someone had stolen all the benches and torn down the roof. The bus stop sign was gone too, so there was no way to know that it was a bus stop. Even the bus drivers sometimes passed it without stopping.

    "Thanks for all the nice presents," BeeJees said to Ed, patting the new knitted cap on his head. "You really surprised us."

    Ed smiled. He had given presents to almost everyone on Ghost Avenue earlier in the morning.

    "You're welcome. Sorry, it was all just cheap stuff."

"Naah, good enough for us." BeeJees had noticed the one last present on Ed's lap. "Who's present is that? The cat's?"

Ed took a glance at the red-and-white paper bag on his lap and shook his head.

"No. I already gave the cat a present." Ed pointed at the cat a few feet away. "A whole blueberry pie."

The cat had its head half-buried in a big pie. It noticed and raised its head for a moment, but immediately went back to the pie.

"This one was for Willy," Ed said as he pulled a light pink muffler out of the bag.

"Oh... Yeah," BeeJees nodded.

They sat in silence for a moment.

Snow had covered most of Everville before dawn. The snow fell at a steady pace throughout the morning. Some wind had started to blow, but the weather was reasonably calm. It was still far from a storm.

"Well, don't worry," BeeJees said to Ed. "You already gave Willy a much bigger present."

"Maybe," Ed said, a sad smile on his face.

BeeJees couldn't find anything else to say, so he let his eyes wander off across the street to the old department store on the corner. The building had been closed since the late seventies. The doors were nailed shut, the windows were boarded up, and everything else was broken.

"That store there," BeeJees said abruptly. "It's just a dump now, but you should have seen it when I was a kid. Every Sunday, musicians played on that patio. My dad used to take me to see them when he wasn't drunk. Me and my baby sister each got an ice cream cone from that booth there. They had the best strawberry ice cream ever."

Ed looked at the patio BeeJees was talking about. There were still a few rusty chairs and tables lying around, but it was hard to imagine the patio when it was new. It was just like the rest of Ghost Avenue. A place left behind and forgotten by time.

"Everything seemed to shine in those days." BeeJees sighed, but with a smile still on his face. "But everything ends, sooner or later. Shops close, towns move away... and people... people die. That's just the way it is. There's nothing we can do to stop it."

The snow kept falling without any sound. It fell on both the rich and the poor. It fell on all things old and new. It fell on anything and everything, hiding the world under a soft white cover.

"Sometimes," BeeJees said in a sad but gentle tone. "Sometimes, we just have to let go.(手を放す)"

Ed noticed that BeeJees' voice sounded a little bit like Willy's. It brought him some comfort(安心感).

In a peculiar(奇妙な) way, Willy had survived, Ed thought. *Inside BeeJees. Inside himself. Inside them all.*

"Some things, we can't change. But some things, we *can* change. You should know," BeeJees said. "You taught us."

Ed nodded. After a pause(ちょっとの間), he said to BeeJees.

"I'm going to the mall on the two o'clock bus. You know, about the shop in the Food Court."

"Good idea," BeeJees said, stretching his arms. "Hope everything goes really great."

"I'm going to decline(辞退する) the offer(申し出)."

"What?"

"I already have a shop here," Ed said. "Besides, they told me I would have to move away from Ghost Avenue if I wanted the shop. Some rule in the health code, they said. And if I rent(借りる) an apartment, I won't be able to take the cat with me."

The cat raised an eyebrow(まゆ). It seemed to know they were talking about it. The empty pie plate(皿) from the blueberry pie was lying at the cat's feet.

"Well, it's your life." BeeJees shrugged.

Ed was about to reply when a voice rang out from above them.

"Yo! Everything's ready to go, man!"

It was George. He had appeared on the roof of the old department store holding the end of an electric cable. The other end of the cable was connected to a telephone pole in the street.

Many of the Ghosts heard George's voice. They came out from their usual hiding places into the street. BeeJees stood up and gave George a thumbs-up sign.

"Okay, George. Hit the switch!" BeeJees shouted.

"Gotcha!" George replied. He disappeared behind the edge of the roof. The crowd waited in silence. Ed stood up too, unable to hide his excitement.

Another moment passed in the quiet of the snow, and then suddenly, the roof of the department store lit up with Christmas lights. A loud applause rose up from Ghost Avenue. Everybody yelled "Merry Christmas!"

George started singing a Christmas tune. Within seconds, most of the others joined in, and the street became one big Christmas choir. BeeJees and Ed smiled at each other.

"It's not anything like the good old days, but it's a lot better than nothing," BeeJees said.

The lights were just cheap toy lights bought at the nearest supermarket, and the electricity was illegally pulled from the telephone pole, but the moment was so wonderful that no one cared. After many long years of silence, Christmas had finally returned to Ghost Avenue.

Standing amid the snow, song, and laughter, BeeJees said once again, softly.

"Yeah. Some things... you *can* change."

BFC : THE FINAL EPISODE

THE SNOW OF THE CENTURY

"Look, cat," Ed said to the cat once again. The cat just frowned. "I told you. You can't come with me today."

It was ten minutes after two o'clock. The bus had arrived late. Ed had put one foot up on the step of the bus. The cat was just below Ed, looking up at him with an annoyed expression. It was mad because Ed was blocking its rightful path.

"You have to stay here. I'll be back soon."

The cat snarled. It was tired of Ed blocking its way, so it decided to get on the bus.

"Shut the door! Please!" Ed yelled to the bus driver.

"What?" the bus driver replied in a frustrated tone.

The cat was about to jump on the bus.

"Shut the door, now!" Ed repeated.

The driver finally pulled the door lever, grumbling to himself. The door slammed shut just as the cat was getting ready to leap. The cat's eyes widened as it watched the door close. It became angry when it saw Ed standing on the other side of the door.

The cat kept its eyes on Ed as the bus started to drive away. Ed tried to say something to the cat, but the door was too thick.

From inside the bus, Ed watched the cat grow smaller and smaller in the distance as the bus hurried down the street. The cat was still looking at him when the bus rounded a corner several seconds later.

An absurd question suddenly popped into Ed's head.

What if I never see that cat again?

He frowned and shook it off immediately.

Of course I'll see the cat again. Why not?

But all during the bus ride to the New Mall, the image of the cat sitting there alone on the street came back to him again and again and never really disappeared.

The snow was still falling quite lightly when the bus reached the New Mall some twenty minutes later. As the bus crossed the parking lot, Ed could see the empty space where the Pie Festival had been held.

All the tents and rides were already gone and only a few trailers and trucks still remained there. Somehow, it all seemed like one big dream now.

Inside the mall, it was Christmas everywhere. A chorus of Christmas songs greeted Ed, and Christmas lights decorated almost everything in sight. The movie theater near the entrance was showing a romantic comedy featuring a blue snowman.

There were a lot of people in front of the theater waiting for the next showing. A child recognized Ed's face and hollered, "Hey! You're that mustard pie guy!" The child's parents quickly seized him. Ed blushed and walked on. This happened several more times before he reached the Food Court.

A giant Christmas tree was standing in the middle of the Food Court. It was decorated with real cookies and candy from stores in the mall. Zombie Pies was doing an "Evil Santa Pie-Fest."

Ed's feet stopped when he saw the vacant storefront in the Food Court. The steel shutters outside the shop were pulled down.

Ed sat down on a bench in front of the shop. It was the same bench he had sat on a month before. As he looked at the vacant shop, the idea that perhaps everything had been a dream came back to him again.

This can't be real. Maybe I fell asleep on the bench that day, and had a long, long dream. Maybe I'm still on that bench…

For some reason, the thoughts reminded Ed of the paper inside Willy's fortune cookie. He dug into his pocket and found it. It still said the same thing.

Most treasures are in the places you first find them.

Ed raised his head to look at the shop again. Then, he read the words once more.

…in the places you first find them.

It was almost as if Willy was congratulating him. He knew that wasn't possible, but for a moment, Ed actually believed that it might be.

"Ed! Ed Wishbone! I'm so glad you came."

Ed's heart skipped a beat when the owner suddenly patted him on the shoulder. He was so absorbed in his thoughts that he hadn't realized the owner was standing right beside him. Ed quickly folded the fortune paper and slid it back into his pocket.

"Sir. Good afternoon," Ed said, standing up from the bench.

"Did the snow give you any trouble?" The owner asked Ed in his usual joyous tone. "I sure hope not. Now come with me and I'll show you your new shop."

"Uh... sir, I..."

Ed tried to speak, but the owner went straight to the closed shutters. Ed hurried after him, still not sure how to explain.

"Just a second, while I open this shutter here..." the owner said, turning a key in the lock.

"Sir. I'm sorry. I have something to..."

Ed felt his stomach tighten. He imagined what the owner would say when he told him he didn't want the shop. But if he was going to say it, now was his only chance.

"Here we go," the owner said, and threw open the shutters.

The shutters rolled away, revealing an elegant counter with an open kitchen behind it. The owner turned on the lights and waved his hand towards the inside of the shop.

"Well?"

Ed was speechless. His eyes were wide open. The owner noticed this and smiled. He grabbed Ed's arm and pulled him inside.

"C'mon inside. Take a look."

Ed walked into the shop in a daze.

"Wow..." he whispered. Everything in the shop looked perfect.

"The last tenant was a pastry shop. They left everything behind... so you can open your shop at any time," the owner explained.

Ed nodded, but he wasn't really hearing any of the words.

"Is that the kitchen?" Ed asked.

"It sure is."

"Can I take a look?"

"Of course you can. It's your kitchen."

The owner stepped aside, and Ed moved into the kitchen. Hidden behind the beautiful glass counter were countless pots and pans, kitchen utensils, and spice jars. Ed touched the counter. He stroked its surface softly. It was smooth and spotless.

"This... is all mine?"

"Yes," the owner replied. "All you have to do is sign the contract."

Ed finally recovered his voice, but now, he wasn't sure what to say. He took a long deep breath and said to the owner, "I have to tell you something."

The owner smiled his jolly smile.

"Sure. Anything."

"I..."

I can't accept this prize. I already have a shop.

Ed tried to say, but the words wouldn't come out. The place of his dreams surrounded him in all its hope and splendor. Ed's voice trembled as he finished the sentence.

"I... uh... thank you. Thank you for everything."

"My pleasure," the owner said, laughing. "I'm looking forward to having your pie with lunch everyday."

The owner handed Ed a contract from his coat pocket and patted him on the shoulder.

"Just sign that and bring it to my office before Wednesday. See you then."

Ed couldn't help staring at the contract. When he finally raised his head, the owner was already gone. He was there alone with the contract.

Ed closed his eyes tight. He hated himself. He realized he had completely forgotten about Ghost Avenue for the past few minutes.

"So the little youngster wants Evil Santa, huh?"

Jeremy stood behind the Zombie Pies counter with red and purple makeup on his face, grinning down at a half-scared, half-happy boy who was waiting for his pie.

"Well, Evil Santa wants you too!" Jeremy suddenly raised his voice and a Santa head with a wicked smile popped up from under the counter. The child and his mother both screamed.

So did Ed. Louder.

"AAAGGGHHHH!"

Jeremy was shaken by the scream. He stared at Ed in dumb surprise. Ed had been watching from behind the mother and child. Their eyes met as Ed turned red with embarrassment.

"Oh, it's you," Jeremy said with a sigh. He pulled a rope and the Evil Santa disappeared.

"*That* was scary," Ed said, slowly recovering from the shock.

"If you think that was scary, go use the men's room. You'll be screaming for the rest of the day."

"Uh... no thank you," Ed said and pointed at the Slime Bucket Pies displayed under the counter glass. "But can I get one of those pies?"

Jeremy frowned but mumbled "Sure," and reached under the counter. He brought out an empty crust shaped like a bowl, and poured a dip of mint slime into the crust. He handed it to Ed with a wooden spoon. Ed took a taste and almost immediately said,

"This is great!"

Jeremy just shrugged.

"This is the best chocolate mint pie I've ever had," Ed repeated.

Jeremy thought Ed was being sarcastic, but Ed really seemed to mean it. *Too bad for Wishbone,* he thought, *because by the time he opens his shop, Zombie Pies will be gone.*

This was his shop's last week. Jeremy's father had sold the shop to the Everville Rehabilitation Project. But he didn't tell this to Ed.

"You are one strange person," Jeremy mumbled, but not in a bad tone. "Oh, yeah... do you remember my bodyguard?"

"Sure," Ed said rather uneasily. "Of course."

"He was arrested this morning."

"He was?"

"The arrest wasn't a surprise. He did a lot of *stuff* for my father." Jeremy said the word 'stuff' in a disgusted way. "The real surprise was that the police were able to catch him. He's not an easy man to catch, you know. I think maybe he wanted to get caught."

"Why?" Ed asked.

Jeremy shrugged again. He also knew that if Billy Bob was caught, his father's arrest was not far away, but that was another thing he didn't tell Ed.

"Beats me. I just think so. He didn't like his job very much." As an afterthought, Jeremy added, "He grew up on Ghost Avenue, you know."

Ed thought about this for a moment, but couldn't think of anything to say.

"So when are you going to open?" Jeremy asked, pretending not to look very interested.

Ed smiled awkwardly for a moment.

"I don't deserve that shop," he said.

Jeremy frowned at Ed while serving another customer a slice of pie.

Ed said again, "It's too good for me."

"Yeah, yeah. Of course you don't deserve it. Everyone knows that," Jeremy said. "You only beat me and sixteen other bakers! Sure, you don't deserve it!"

Ed realized what he was saying and added in a hurry, "Oh, no no! I didn't mean it that way... Sorry. I'm really proud about winning the contest! I really am! But that shop... it's just way out of my league."

"I know, Wishbone, I know."

Jeremy seemed a bit angry, but his voice was calm.

"So I'll tell you what you don't know," Jeremy said as he took the dirty spoon back from Ed. "The only thing worse than getting a chance you don't deserve, is wasting that chance."

Ed fell silent. Jeremy stuck his palm out to Ed. Ed didn't understand why and just stared at Jeremy's palm for a moment.

"$2.55 for the pie," Jeremy said flatly.

"Oh... sorry." Ed fumbled in his pocket and pulled out three dollar-bills in a hurry.

"Thank you very much." Jeremy took the money and reached under the counter for change. "Here's your change," he said and squeezed green slime out from his hand into Ed's palm.

"AAAAAAGHHHHHH!"

This scream was even louder.

The six o'clock bus was the last bus, but Ed decided to take the five o'clock bus home. This turned out to be a very good idea, because once the sun set, the snow and wind rapidly grew stronger. When Ed got off the bus, the snow on the ground was already up to his ankles. It was only a short walk back to the theater, but it took him nearly ten minutes to reach the entrance.

"Reporting live from the New Everville Mall, this is Glen Hamperton bringing you coverage of the Christmas celebration events scheduled for tonight."

The voice from the radio greeted Ed as he closed the door against the snow. Ed followed the sound of the radio across the lobby, and into the main theater. George was the first one to notice Ed's return.

"Yo, Ed. You made it just in time, man. We were getting kinda worried."

"Sorry," Ed said as he brushed the snow from his head and shoulders. "The snow's getting worse by the minute."

George, BeeJees, Paddy, Frank, and a few other Ghosts were huddled around the campfire. Frank was holding his new radio in his lap with the volume turned up.

"We were listening to the radio," BeeJees said. "They're doing live from the mall."

Ed nodded and smiled. Glen Hamperton continued to talk. She was introducing a local choir group.

George got up and went to the large, steaming pot that sat beside the campfire. He grabbed a tin cup and dipped it into the pot.

"C'mon, man. We made you some stew," he said to Ed.

Ed sat down beside BeeJees and took the cup from George. Warm, homemade stew with large chunks of vegetables. It was perfect for a day like this.

"So you gave them the bad news?" BeeJees asked as Ed sipped some stew from the cup.

Ed paused for a moment to shake his head.

"I couldn't. I'm planning to go back tomorrow."

BeeJees nodded silently. The radio had started to broadcast a Christmas chorus.

"Cat, cat, cat. Fat, fat, fat," Frank sang along with his own words. He was singing to a poster he had found somewhere.

"You got the roof repaired in time," Ed said to George. He realized that no snow was falling from above. Several wide planks of wood had been laid across the roof, covered with some sort of plastic sheet.

"Yeah. Paddy helped me," George answered proudly, and exchanged a high-five with Paddy.

"Cat fat fat, big fat cat."

Ed couldn't help smiling as he listened to Frank's song. It was so peaceful here. He couldn't believe that it was just a day ago that Willy had passed away. Ed knew that all of them were still sad, but everyone seemed to just go on with their normal life. They had all cried, they had all said good-bye, and now, they all seemed to know that it was time to move on.

It seemed a little strange to Ed, who had thought that after someone you loved died, you were supposed to be sad for a period (一定期間) of time. At least, he had been sad for years, when his mother had passed away. — But he liked the attitude (受け止める)姿勢 here better. For some reason, it seemed a lot more natural.

Some things we can't change.

Ed took a sip (ひとくち) of stew as he looked over at Willy's stroller (ベビーカー) sitting alone by the wall. It would probably stay there for a long time to come.

Ed had asked the driver of the silent ambulance (救急車) where he was taking Willy. The driver had answered, "I have no idea." It had all been sad. But sitting there with the Ghosts, in a town that had a very vague sense of time, it didn't feel as sad as it had seemed at first. It was just the way it was.

Ed felt the warmth of the campfire once again. He felt ashamed of forgetting, even for a short time, how warm it was here. The gentle taste of George's stew. The flickering of the campfire. Frank's funny song. And the slow, almost frozen sense of time inside the theater...

Everything he needed was here. He shook his head as he finished the stew. *What was he thinking?* He had to be careful. He had to think real hard because it was...

Ed suddenly stood up in alarm.

His face had become very serious. He looked around the theater a second time. Finding nothing there, he started towards the lobby.

"Ed. What's the matter?"

Ed ignored George's question and rushed into the lobby. He came back only a moment later, much more pale than before.

"George," Ed said.

"Where's the cat?"

"Mommy. There was a kitty walking in the snow," the girl said to her mother from the back seat of her family car.

"What did you say, Jane?" her mother asked from the passenger seat in front.

"I saw a kitty-cat walking in the snow," the girl repeated.

"Don't be silly, Jane. Look at how thick the snow is."

"But I know I saw one. It was a big kitty!"

"It was probably just a fire hydrant or something. A cat would freeze to death in this weather."

The girl looked outside again. She knew that her mother was right. But she also knew for sure that she had seen a big fat cat walking along the road. She had even seen the cat's eyes as it looked back at her.

"I just hope kitty's alright," she whispered.

Only the wind answered, with a high shrill cry.

"...the storm has now entered the Spyglass district and heavy snow is falling from the sky. The storm is expected to develop into a blizzard soon..."

The emergency weather forecast poured out of the radio as Ed, BeeJees, George, and Paddy gathered in the lobby. Everyone was covered with snow from head to foot. They looked at each other without hope.

"BeeJees?" Ed asked.

"Nope. Nowhere," BeeJees answered. "George, did you look around the junkyard?"

"Yeah. It's already covered with snow. No footsteps."

A heavy silence filled the lobby. Only Frank, who seemed not to understand the circumstances, kept singing the cat song he had made up.

"The mall," Ed said. "Maybe he came after me."

Ed checked the only working clock in the theater.

"The last bus is due (来る) 予定の in about five minutes. I have to go."

George and Paddy looked at each other, then grabbed hold of Ed's arms so he couldn't run off.

"Ed, man! Wait a minute," BeeJees said.

"I have to find the cat! He'll freeze to death in this weather!"

"You'll freeze to death first!" BeeJees shouted. "If you take the last bus to the mall, how are you going to get back? You sure as hell can't *walk* in this weather!"

Ed wasn't listening. Paddy held Ed tighter, thinking he was going to run towards the door, but Ed was staring at something else.

"Frank," Ed said, blinking (まばたきする) his eyes.

"Frank?" BeeJees asked with a puzzled look.

They all followed Ed's eyes to Frank. Frank was still singing his cat song to the poster he held. Ed loosened (ゆるめる) George and Paddy's grips and walked over to Frank.

"Frank." Ed started to reach for the poster Frank was holding. "Where did you get this?"

"Outside," Frank replied with a smile. "Good man give me."

"Today?" Ed asked again.

"Uh-huh." Frank pointed happily at the poster. "Cat!"

BeeJees and George came beside Ed and took a look at the poster. They held their breath.

"Oh no..." Ed whispered.

Ed grabbed the poster. As soon as he read the first two lines, he headed for the door. George and BeeJees ran after Ed and seized him just as he was about to step outside.

"Let me go! I have to go! He's my cat!"

"Ed!" BeeJees said to him in a desperate tone grabbing him by the collar. The weather outside was really dangerous. BeeJees knew he had to stop him. He shouted in Ed's face, "ED!"

Ed stopped struggling. His face was frozen with fear.

BeeJees spoke as calmly as he could, "Ed. Listen. Do you really think that anyone can catch that cat? I think... maybe the cat *knew*."

Ed's face grew stern as he heard those words.

"I know it sounds crazy! But... but maybe... Maybe the cat knew that you couldn't take him with you. Maybe he left because he wanted you to have that shop in the mall!"

Ed lowered his arms. BeeJees let go. Ed staggered back a step, not saying a word.

He had forgotten about the cat.

He was so selfish that he had forgotten all about the cat.

He looked around the lobby at everyone's worried faces, then closed his eyes.

"Damn!" Ed hit his hand hard on the ruins of the ticket counter.

"What am I doing? *What am I doing!*" he shouted.

Full of anger at himself, Ed reached into his pocket, took out the contract from the New Mall, and ripped it into shreds. He threw the pieces on the floor.

"I'm sorry," Ed said.

And before anybody could move, Ed shoved George back with both hands and ran through the door.

"Ed!" BeeJees shouted after Ed, but George bumped into him and they both fell down. When they finally got back to their feet, Ed had already disappeared into the snow.

George and BeeJees stood at the front door of the theater, helplessly looking out into the snowstorm. The snow was no longer a romantic ornament for the streets. It was now a dangerous enemy.

Behind them, Frank's radio continued to give the weather forecast in a flat, emotionless tone.

"...the wind has now reached forty miles per hour and it is very dangerous to walk outside..."

A half hour later, Ed arrived at the New Mall and went straight to the pay phone near the entrance. He found the number of the Everville Health Center on the poster and dialed it. After the tenth ring, a man's voice finally answered. The man seemed tired and reluctant（気が進まない）to talk. Ed hurriedly explained what had happened.

"Yes. Big, dark, mean（意地悪な）... It's usually walking around Ghost Avenue. Yes! Yes! That's my cat," Ed cried into the phone excitedly. "Have you caught him?"

The passing customers all stared at Ed with suspicious（けげんな）looks on their faces. Ed lowered his voice a little.

"Yes... near Ghost Avenue... Yes... and did you... You chased him for four blocks!?" Ed shouted into the phone. He lowered his voice again after a few middle-aged women pointed at him. "But... but he escaped?"

Half relieved（安心して）and half disappointed, Ed took a deep breath. The man on the other end seemed outraged（激怒する）.

"Yes... yes. Sir, I'm really sorry the cat ripped your new jacket... yes, and your new pants... and of course, sir, I'll be glad to pay for the belt too, but could you please tell me where you saw him last? Sir? Sir? Please don't hang up!"

But the man hung up. Ed put the phone back down on the hook. He turned from the phone, and almost walked straight into Jeremy, who was standing behind him. Jeremy was dressed to leave work. He had a cell phone in his hand.

"I thought you already went home," Jeremy said, adding in a sarcastic tone, "Or at least something like a home."

Ed stared at Jeremy for a moment. Then he showed him the poster.

"My cat's lost."

Jeremy looked at the poster without much thought. As he read the lines, his frown grew deeper, and finally froze into an expression of horror. He spoke to Ed in a low voice.

"Wishbone. This isn't good news. You could be disqualified[失格になる] for this."

"I don't care."

"Of course you do! This might be your only real chance in life and you..."

Jeremy realized that Ed wasn't looking at him. His eyes were glued to a small crowd that was developing at the center of the mall. The reporter, Glen Hamperton, was in the middle of the crowd with a microphone in one hand. There were also several television cameras moving among the crowd. It was probably the program George and BeeJees had been listening to on the radio.

"Wishbone! Listen to me!"

Jeremy grabbed Ed to make him look his way. Ed did, but his eyes didn't stop on Jeremy's face. They stopped on the cell phone he was holding. An idea had come to his mind.

"Wishbone! I said..."

"I have to borrow this," Ed said, and without waiting for an answer, took the phone from Jeremy's hand. Jeremy opened his mouth wide in annoyance as he watched Ed examine the phone.

"Is this the number for the phone?" Ed asked Jeremy, showing him the phone number taped on the side with cellophane tape.

"Yes. I have so many phones that..."

"Thanks," Ed said and ran off towards the crowd of people.

"Wishbone! Hey, wait a minute! Damn it!"

It took another moment for Jeremy to sigh and run after Ed. By the time Jeremy arrived at the edge of the crowd, Ed was squeezing between people, trying to get to the stage in the middle. Jeremy bit on his lower lip.

"Wishbone... What the hell(強調) are you doing?"

Jeremy followed after Ed but was blocked by a group of teenagers who wanted to shake his hand. Jeremy fought them off, but by the time he escaped, Ed had already climbed onto the stage. Guards came forward to stop him, but Glen Hamperton recognized Ed immediately.

"Look who we have here, everyone! The winner of the state pie contest, Ed Wishbone!"

The crowd cheered, thinking Ed was a guest on the show. Ed ignored them and went straight towards Glen.

"Well, what brings you here today, Ed?"

Glen pointed the microphone towards Ed.

"I'm sorry," was all Ed said before he took the microphone from Glen's hand. Glen stared in pure surprise as Ed stepped in front of her to face directly into the camera.

"I'm sorry to interrupt. But this is something very important to me," Ed said, his voice shaking with urgency.

The crowd around the stage heard the serious tone in his voice. The cheering and shouting died down. Ed took a deep breath and held the poster up to the camera.

"My cat is lost in the snow somewhere," he said as the camera focused on the poster. "I need your help. Everyone's help."

In that one moment, the picture of the cat was broadcast to every house in Everville. Snowed-in families sitting in their living rooms watching television all moved closer to the screen to get a better look.

The owner of the New Mall happened to be watching television in his office with a beer in hand. He sprayed his beer all over his desk when he saw the poster.

Jeremy covered his eyes with his right hand and moaned.

On Ghost Avenue, George, Paddy, and BeeJees all crowded around the radio unable to believe what they were hearing. BeeJees dropped his mug on the ground and whispered, "Oh, shit."

"If you have seen this cat, please call me at 555-22xx. This is the cat that ruined the first round of the pie contest yesterday. The health center is chasing him. I didn't know any of this until today. I'm really sorry, and I'm fully responsible for the situation. I'll give back all my prize money and disclaim ownership of the shop in the New Mall as soon as possible."

Ed looked straight into the camera and said to the people of Everville.

"But right now, I have to find my cat. That's all that matters."

A silence followed as Ed stared into the camera for a moment. Nobody in the crowd moved.

After taking a deep breath, Ed gave the microphone back to Glen and stepped off the stage. The crowd remained frozen in position. Ed was sure that everyone was angry at him. He didn't look up.

But after a moment, a woman began clapping her hands. Then a man joined in. A brief pause followed, and then, several other people started clapping their hands. Ed looked around. He was so dumbfounded that he bumped into a bleak-faced Jeremy as he stepped out of the crowd.

"What the hell was that?" Jeremy asked in an angry voice.

"I need to borrow your phone for a while," Ed said.

"Forget the phone, you idiot! Do you know what you've done? You just threw away the best chance of your life!"

Ed gave him one short nod and headed down the aisle. Jeremy followed along, shouting at him.

"What stupid reason was that for? The cat doesn't even have a collar! Anybody would have thought it was a stray! Why did you have to say on TV that it was your cat?"

Ed didn't slow down for a second. He was headed straight outside. Jeremy sighed, shook his head, and with a slight change of tone in his voice, continued shouting at Ed.

"And what are you going to do without a car? Walk!? It's nine degrees below zero outside, you nitwit!"

Ed finally came to a stop by the exit. The snow had become even fiercer in the last few minutes. The weather outside was so violent that even Ed, despite his determination, had to stop for a moment.

"You're really going to choose a cat over a shop in the mall?" Jeremy asked Ed one last time.

"The cat... *he* chose me," Ed replied.

"You're so damn stupid, it's almost illegal," Jeremy said, as he pulled out his car keys and headed for the door. "You wait here."

When Jeremy opened the door, the snowstorm noticed, and attacked full force. Jeremy winced, but stood his ground. The last thing he did before stepping out into the snow was to say to Ed,

"And you better check on that '*he*' part."

Ed watched in surprise, as Jeremy dashed through the snow to his car. He wanted to thank him, but he had no time to do that now.

The snowstorm had arrived.

"Okay folks, I have a message here from one of our listeners."

"Hello, SRN. I'm a college student visiting my grandparents in Everville for winter vacation. It's been a great Christmas for me. All the family together, delicious homemade dinners, watching a lot of old movies, a warm fireplace, and a whole bunch of presents!"

"I have to tell you… Christmas is the best time of year."

Jeremy's black limousine fought through the snow, swerving and sliding, as they drove south on Valley Mills Drive. The car routinely skidded sideways off the road, flinging Ed across the back seat countless times. He sat up quickly but was soon flung again, and each time he banged his head into something hard.

"Please keep the car steady!"

Ed cried to Jeremy from the back seat after a fifth encounter with the back door. Jeremy, driving with almost zero visibility, shouted back angrily.

"It would help if you closed the damn window! We're going to catch pneumonia!"

Snow was blowing in through the back window. Driving the limousine was even more difficult with snow swirling not only outside, but inside the car too.

Ed kept his eyes on the roadside with his head poking halfway out the window. But it was impossible to spot a single cat in this snow. Ed's lips had gone from blue to black, and he could barely keep his eyes open in the cold wind. Hope ran out of him with every passing second.

Jeremy took a glance at Ed and saw the desperate look on his face. He swallowed once.

"Look, I don't want to sound cruel, but I'm sure you've realized by now that if the cat were still outside, it would already be dead."

Jeremy took another look in the rearview mirror. Ed seemed not to have heard what Jeremy had said.

"Wishbone! Are you listening, dammit? We could easily die out here too, you know!"

Ed bit on his lower lip. The big roadside sign for the New Mall stood on the other side of the road. Everything beneath it was already buried in the snow. He knew Jeremy was right. They could have passed the cat anywhere. His mind told him it was pointless.

But the image of the cat sitting there on the street earlier today, and the image of that same cat lying beneath cold snow, slowly freezing to death, wouldn't allow Ed to give up.

Some things you can change.

He had to believe. He was so damn tired of losing everything.

Jeremy's cell phone suddenly rang. Ed fumbled for the phone. It took him a moment to press the talk button with his cold fingers. It was a short but horrible moment for Ed. He was scared that the caller might hang up.

"It's probably just another crank call," Jeremy muttered.

"Hello?" Ed said into the phone. "Hello?"

There was some background noise, but no voice at the other end. It seemed like another hoax. There had been five of them already. But this time, after a long pause, a small girl's voice came from the speaker.

"I saw your kitty," the girl said. "It was walking down Valley Mills Drive. Near the big sign for the mall."

"Valley Mills Drive? Here!?" Ed repeated. They had just passed that 'big sign' moments ago. "Could you tell me when...?"

But the phone was already dead. The child had hung up, perhaps she was too shy or scared to talk anymore.

"Thank you," Ed said softly into the phone and rushed to the window once again. He said to Jeremy, "A girl called. She said she saw my cat somewhere near here!"

"And of course you believe her," Jeremy said in a sarcastic tone.

Ed went back and forth across the car trying to spot something — any sign of the cat. Jeremy opened his window too. The snow flew through the car now, making the inside of the car almost the same as the outside. They looked and looked, but all they could see was white land.

Ed spotted the sign for the sandwich shop he had stopped at. He could almost see a phantom image of himself and the cat on the roadside, still looking for a new job.

Everything that had happened since then — both the good and the bad — the cat had always been there with him. The image of the cat lying dead in the snow rose up in his mind again, and he closed his eyes to fight the tears.

"Willy..." Ed said, almost like a prayer. It was the only word he knew that seemed stronger than the despair outside. And that very name brought something back into his mind.

The fortune paper.

Something told him to take the paper out of his pocket and read it one final time. So he did that.

Most treasures are in the places you first find them.

And this time, the words made perfect sense. Ed jumped to the window again and stuck his head out as far as he could. The snow attacked him fiercely, but about a hundred feet ahead, he was able to see the road fork towards Old Everville — towards the Outside Mall.

It wasn't about the shop, Ed thought. *It never was.*

"Turn left at the next corner!" Ed said to Jeremy.

"What!?" Jeremy thought he'd heard wrong.

The road to the left at the traffic signal was very narrow and was already deeply covered in snow. It wasn't even a road anymore. It was just a pile of snow.

"I need to get to the Outside Mall. Turn left at that corner. It's over the hill."

"That corner?" Jeremy shouted, pointing at the nonexistent 存在しない road ahead. "*That corner!?* You're insane! 狂っている We'll get stranded 遭難する and die!"

Ed took a deep breath and calmly said,

"Then let me out at the corner."

"You're kidding." からかう

"I'm not. Pull over by the side and I'll get off."

The corner was approaching 近づく fast. A precious moment passed before Jeremy was able to say anything.

"Now, wait a minute. Let's consider 検討する this again. You want me to drive this extra fancy limo (limousine) *into that pool of snow*?!"

The corner was now moments away. Jeremy caught a glimpse 一瞬見えた映像 of Ed getting ready to go out into the snow and spoke faster.

"Do you know what this car cost?! The front bumper probably cost more than everything in your bank account! And look! This new audio system cost something like... damn! TO HELL WITH IT! I'M RICH ANYWAY!"

Jeremy yanked the steering wheel to the left and the car spun off towards Old Everville, crashing head first into the heavy drift.

"And now the road down to Standpoint is completely cut off. All public transportation in the Spyglass area has been halted. Please remain indoors until further notice..."

Frank's radio kept repeating the same message over and over. BeeJees, George, and Paddy all sat around the fire, looking glumly at the radio. The wind shook the old theater to its foundations, reminding them how dangerous it was outside.

BeeJees sighed.

"There's no way the cat could still be alive."

No one answered. George and Paddy tended the fire in sad silence. BeeJees stared at the floor.

"Uh-uh," someone said.

BeeJees raised his eyes and looked at George and Paddy, but both shook their heads. It wasn't either of them. The voice had come from behind BeeJees.

"Uh-uh," Frank said again, smiling his toothless smile. He was rolling around in his wagon.

"What, Frank?" BeeJees said, a little annoyed.

Frank gave them all a big proud smile and said,

"Eddie findie cat."

They all stared at each other. Frank nodded to himself as if he were sure. Then he looked at Willy's stroller and nodded a second time. With a great big smile, he pointed straight towards Old Everville and repeated in a confident voice.

"Ed always findie cat."

The car had run off the road near the top of the hill. It landed in a ditch(道ばたの 溝), one tire buried deep in the snow. The engine was still alive, but the headlights were both smashed(つぶれた).

Ed opened the back door of the limousine and stepped out into the snow. He had hit his head. His right temple(こめかみ) was bleeding a little.

He peered(のぞく) inside the car to check if Jeremy was okay. Jeremy seemed to be shaken-up(ショックを受けた), but he wasn't injured(けがをする). Ed sighed with relief, but before Jeremy could recover enough to stop him, he started walking down the hill, straight into the snowstorm.

The snow came up to his knees, and it was difficult to walk even a few steps. The wind threatened his balance and the blowing snow suffocated him. But he didn't stop. He waded forward, digging through the snow, fighting his way down the hill.

His whole body was so cold. His feet seemed like someone else's feet.

Down below, he could see nothing but white, white, white land. Snow had covered everything. He remembered that the Outside Mall was at the bottom of the hill, but all he could see was snow. Even if the cat were somewhere down there, he had no idea how to find it. But he kept going anyway.

Halfway down the hill, his legs gave out and he fell forward, tumbling down the hill, creating a long cloud of snow in the air. He rolled all the way down, and finally stopped after sliding another few feet across flat ground. He moaned in pain but got up.

"Caaat!" Ed shouted into the blizzard, but the wind erased his voice. He called out even louder, "Caaat! Where are you!? Caaaat!!"

Only the wind answered. Ed was too cold and too tired to think.

The snow was all around him. It came from all directions, completely blinding him. His hands were half-frozen and the cold had entered his lungs. He was losing his sense of direction. He knew he was somewhere near the shop, but everything was hidden under the snow. The world was just one big white blur.

"Cat..." Ed didn't know if he was standing or not. He realized he had closed his eyes sometime before. He was so tired.

"Cat... I'm sorry..."

Then, everything began to fade.

Everything became white with the snow.

Willy?

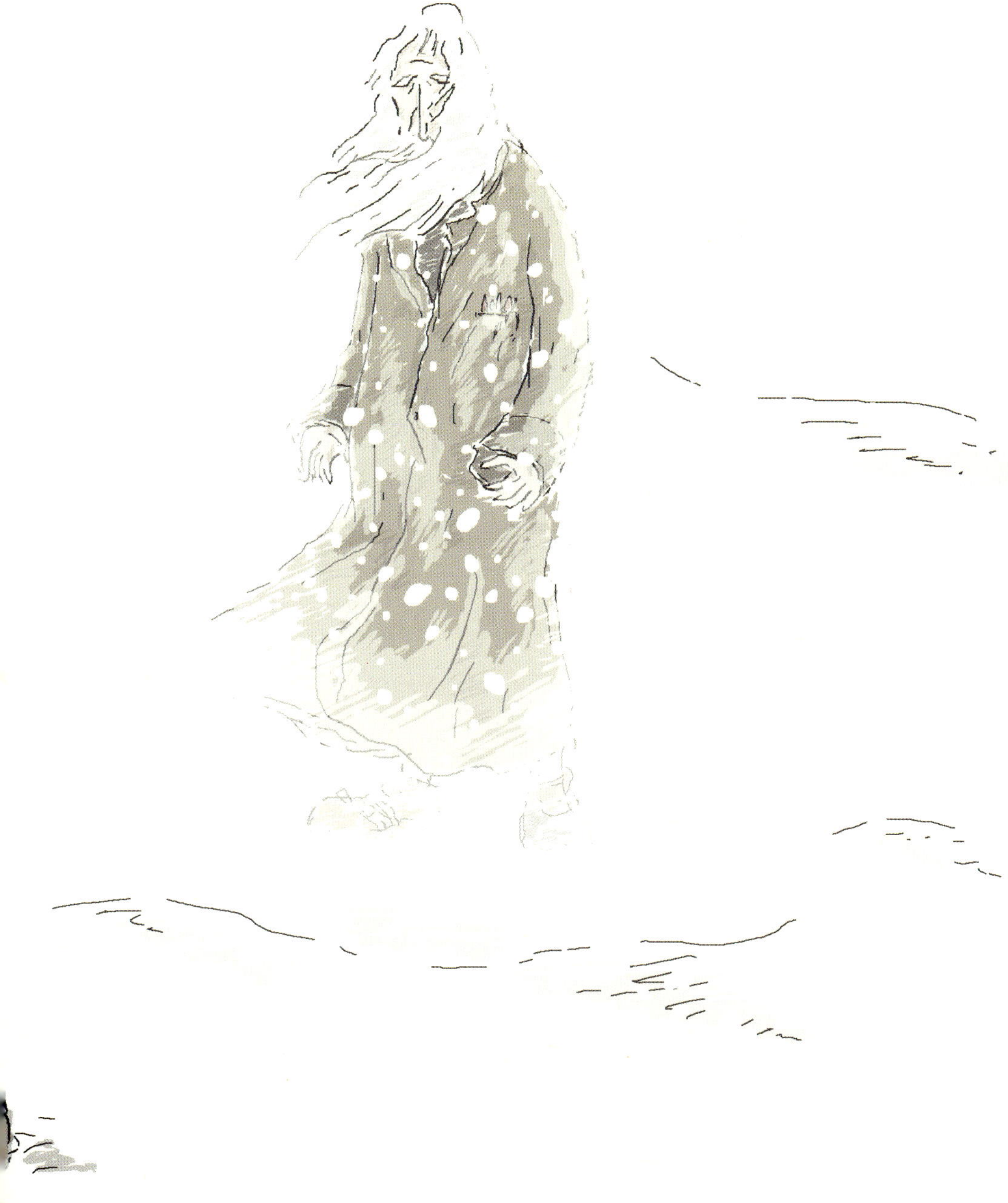

"Son, you're going to freeze to death if you sleep here,"

Willy said with a smile. Ed got to his knees, thinking vaguely,ぼんやりと *you should put on this muffler, Willy. It's really cold today.*

"Willy," Ed said. "I'm sorry. I... I was late again. I'm always late."

Willy smiled.

"No, Ed."

Despite all the wind and snow, Willy's voice was clear and calm. It still had that warm tone.

"You were never late. You've always made it just in time. You found that cat just before it starved飢える to death. You learned a great lesson just before you gave up. You found the real meaning of winning just before you won... And you saved my soul魂... all, just in time."

Ed shook his head.

"No. I... I... Willy... I've lost my cat... I went after him, but I was late again. He saved me. He was always there with me and I was late..."

Willy just stood there smiling.

"No, Ed. I told you. You were always there in time. You just didn't see it that way."

"But Willy... I... I..."

The moon somehow appeared in the sky through the snow. It was the same moon as the one they had seen on the way to the hospital. It was still beautiful. Willy smiled one final time.

"You've always made it in time... and you made it just in time again," said Willy. "Now wake up."

"Willy...?"

Ed opened his eyes halfway and realized he had fainted somewhere in the snow. He was barely able to get to his knees. He looked around for Willy, but there was nothing but the snowstorm around him.

"Willy... I..."

Ed stopped, noticing that he was holding something in his right hand beneath the snow. He pulled his hand out and a string came out from under the snow. He didn't realize what it was for a moment. He just stared at it.

But slowly, very slowly, he realized that he had seen the string before. He pulled the string from under the snow. A ragged gingerbread man was connected to it.

Ed opened his eyes wider and pulled on the string frantically. A line of gingerbread man decorations popped out of the snow in front of him. It was a decoration from Pie Heaven's front window.

Ed got to his feet. The storm seemed to have weakened a little. Ed quickly tugged on the line. The other end was stuck under a snow-covered box a few feet away.

Ed rushed over to the box and wiped the snow off the top of the box. It was his old glass showcase.

Ed used his hands to find the edge of the case. This was the showcase he had always stored his blueberry pies in. He pulled off the top of the case and looked inside. The snow had penetrated the case, filling up half of its interior. Ed dug the snow out with both hands, ignoring the pain in his fingertips. He finally managed to get most of the snow out.

"No..." Ed gasped.

Buried under the snow, in a corner of the case, was a ball of fur.

"Oh no..."

The ball of fur didn't move. Ed knelt down on the snow with trembling hands.

"Cat..." Ed said. The tears he had held back came now. He said in a weak voice, "Cat... wake up... please."

Ed reached out and touched the body of the cat. It was cold. Ed gulped. A shiver ran down his spine.

"Cat... come on. I found you. I found you again. This time, I know I'm not late. Now wake up!"

From the day it had come into Pie Heaven, it had always been his cat. It had preferred his blueberry pies right from the start. It was his one and only cat.

"You can't sleep here, cat! C'mon, I wasn't late, damn it! I swear I wasn't late this time!"

There was no answer. The cat lay perfectly still. But somehow, Ed knew the cat could hear him. The cat had always come back to him, and it would come back, one final time.

"C'mon! I'll bake you all the blueberry pies you want. Just... just wake up. Please. CAT! WAKE UP!"

But still, no response. No response at all. All strength began to run out of Ed. He stood there a while staring at the motionless body of the cat. It seemed so cold lying there in the snow.

Ed took off his muffler and covered the cat. He bent down and picked the cat up, wrapping it inside the muffler. The cat's body was still slightly warm. And heavy. He realized this was the first time he had ever held the cat and it made him cry.

"I'm sorry... I forgot... for a moment there in the mall, I forgot... and you... you probably thought I... I'm sorry, cat."

The cat moved. Ed thought he had imagined it, but the cat slowly looked up at him with a big frown.

"Cat?"

The cat was looking around for blueberry pie and found none. In a very frustrated mood, it glared at Ed for waking it up during a perfectly good nap. It sneezed once and swiftly jumped out of Ed's hands.

Ed was completely frozen for a moment. He stared at the cat with disbelief. The cat was taking a stretch as if nothing had happened.

"Cat...? You're... *okay*?"

The cat yawned. Ed reached out for the cat, but the cat, as always, scratched him.

"You're okay?!" Ed said. "Oh my God. You're okay!"

Ed closed his eyes tightly as great relief rushed through him. It was a moment so unbelievable that he couldn't even breathe for a few seconds. He opened his eyes again and looked at the cat. The cat was still staring at him.

"I come all this way to find you, and you're taking a nap, you damn thing," Ed said with a smile on his face, tears in his eyes and snow in his hair.

As Ed wiped his eyes, he realized that the snow and wind were beginning to calm down. Only a gentle shower of snowflakes was now falling from the sky.

"Cat... all during the time I was searching for you, I was thinking why I needed you so much. And I think I finally know now," Ed said as he knelt down in front of the cat. A beautiful white world enveloped them as they sat there together in the ruins of Pie Heaven.

"Mom gave me the recipe, Willy gave me the courage... but you..." Ed paused.

"You gave me the reason. Even when nobody came to my shop, you were always there to eat my pies. *You* were the one that made me a baker. I would have quit baking a long time ago if it wasn't for you." Ed smiled and said to the cat in a voice that was his most sincere, "Thanks. Thanks a lot."

For a moment, time itself seemed to pause. The world was quiet and forgiving in the silent snowfall. Even then, Ed knew in the back of his mind, that time would start moving again soon. He would have to apologize to a lot of people, and he would also have to find a way to build a new life. But for now, he didn't care. It was only him and the cat — just as it was in the beginning.

Ed stood up.

You are a baker, Ed. Just a baker without a shop. Now go back. Bake your pie.

"I will, Willy," Ed whispered to himself as he wrapped the muffler around him. The cat had become tired of waiting. It decided to scratch Ed again.

"I know, I know. I'll bake you a blueberry pie as soon as we get home. I have to get the Magic Pie Shop ready anyway."

The cat scratched him for an answer. Ed smiled.

"And cat, you really need a name," he said.

The snowstorm had reduced*(減少させる)* all the colors in the world to a big white land of snow. In the distance, a police siren was coming their way. Ed and the cat started walking back towards town, their footsteps lined close together in the snow.

　This night will end, but soon, a new day will begin in the town of Everville.

There are a lot of pies in this world.

Some are sweeter than others.
  Some are sour.
    Some are even spicy or bitter or hot.

But that's not important.
What's important is that every pie is different.
Every pie has its own taste.

My pie may not be sweet — it may seem funny at first sight. But it's all I have, and it's all mine.

*And whatever the pie... whatever the taste...
if you have friends, family, and of course... a cat
you love... that pie will always taste good.*

Even if it is... a mustard pie.

The End

BFC Presents :

Short Story Collection

Moochies 84

Tales from the Red Book: The Hand 86

Look & See 88

The Last Pages of the Red Book 90

A Good Man Is Hard to Find 96

MOOCHIES

I don't want to go.

I'm sorry, Diablo, but your father was transferred to a different station.

But I have friends here!

You can write to them. After all, it's not like you'll die or anything.

Our planet is only a few light years away!

You can leave me here. I'm old enough to live alone.

I've heard that our next planet eats ice cream for lunch.

MOM! Don't forget to pack a big spoon!

Why can't I take my history books with me?

Violent material isn't allowed on our next planet.

What about my video game, 'Bloody Death Combat?'

That's okey.

84

Burbert, you've been a great butler to us.
Thank you, sir.
Since this is our last day, I want to tell you our great secret.
I'm bald.
Goodbye, Earth! Goodbye, everybody!
Don't be sad, Diablo. You can come visit them when you grow up.
You should tell him about the difference in time zone.
It's only two hundred years.
You checked everything, right?
Sure. Twice.
Then why do I get this feeling that we've left something behind?
Hmmm... An unusually quiet day.
CROISSANT
Why do I have this really, really bad feeling?
FOR SALE

TALES FROM THE RED BOOK
THE HAND

One day after his 25th birthday, Victor Scoles saw "the hand" for the first time. It was floating in the air two feet in front of him. At first, he thought it was just a trick of the eye. But the hand didn't disappear, even when he rubbed his eyes until they hurt. When Victor approached it, the hand moved away, always maintaining the same distance from him. It seemed like no one else could see it.

As the days passed, the hand became more and more clear to his eyes. It was always there, from dawn to dusk, waiting for him at every corner of every street. Victor went to an eye doctor, then to a shrink, but both of them told him that it was just stress. Victor tried to ignore the hand. But he grew more and more scared, as days became weeks.

It was as if some evil force were reaching for him, trying to drag him down into a dark death. One day, he realized that he could still see the hand even when he closed his eyes. It never disappeared. He shouted and threw things at the hand, but they just went through it. Soon, he began to see the hand in his dreams. There was now no escape from the hand.

Late one night, Victor decided to take out his hunting rifle and shoot the hand. He hadn't been able to sleep for five days, and his head was hurting very badly. And he was really, really angry. He fired at the hand, but the bullets just passed through it, destroying his house. Victor cursed and screamed and ran after the hand, shooting the rifle again and again.

When the police finally stopped him, Victor had already been shot five times. His body was taken to the police station and was examined for drugs. A few days later, the chief of police announced to the press, that no drugs were found in Victor's body, but that a large tumor was discovered inside his head. The chief speculated maybe it was the reason for his insanity. He finished by saying: "The tumor had a strange shape. It resembled the shape of a human hand."

THE END

LOOK & SEE...

... THROUGH THE WINDOW...

... OF AN AIRPLANE...

... ACROSS THE GALAXY...

... ALONG THE STARS...

... AROUND THE PLANET...

... ON A STICK...

... IN A PARK...

... INSIDE A DOME...

... WITH OTHER MOONS...

... ON THE MOON...

... IN MY ROOM...

... THROUGH THE WINDOW...

... OF AN AIRPLANE...

THE LAST PAGES OF THE RED BOOK

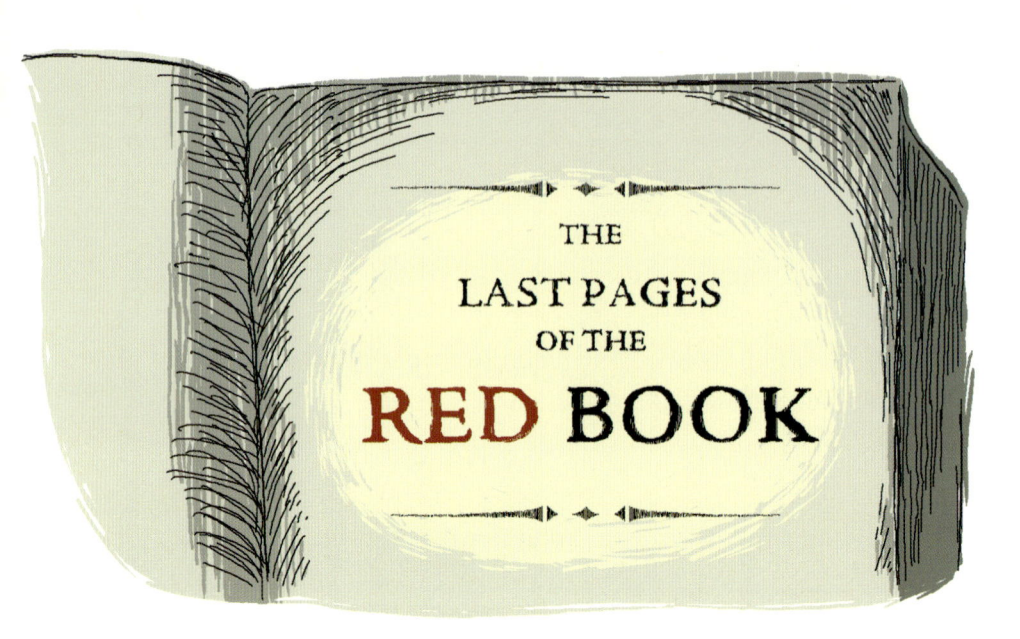

F ather Patrick Gibbons had searched for the Red Book his whole life. His father had been killed with an axe[斧] when he was still a small child, and his mother had been arrested[逮捕される] for his father's murder. But little Patrick knew his mother was innocent[無実], because he had seen it — the scene of his father's death.

His father had brought home an old red book that afternoon, and had been reading it late into the night. When Patrick said good night

90

to his father, his father didn't seem to hear him. His father's eyes were glued [のりづけされる] to the pages of the book. They looked like the eyes of a dead man. Dark, cold eyes just staring into the book.

Hours after going to bed, Patrick could not sleep. He could not forget his father's dark eyes. Finally, he climbed quietly out of bed and walked down the hall to the living room.

Just as Patrick peeked through the keyhole in the living room door, his father turned the last page of the Red Book. What happened next determined [確定する] the rest of Patrick's life.

A dark shadow shaped somehow like an old lady suddenly appeared from behind the armchair his father was sitting in. Patrick watched in horror as the shadow took out a long axe. He wanted to scream, but his body was frozen. A moment later, he saw a horrible image that was burned into his soul [魂] forever.

He would never forget the heavy sound of the axe.

The next thing he knew, it was morning. He was lying in a police station. A police officer told him that his mother had a 'fight' with his father, and that Patrick was going to be put in an orphanage [孤児院].

He tried to explain what he saw through the keyhole, but no one believed him. They never found any 'Red Book' at the scene of the crime [犯罪]. He tried harder and harder to explain, and eventually [やがて], they put him in a mental hospital. He stayed there for two long years.

He learned there, that no one would ever believe his story, and that his parents would never come back.

After he was released from the hospital, Patrick went to a Christian school and became a priest, but he never for one day forgot about the evil Red Book.

Years passed, and Patrick became a respected priest at the Everville Memorial Church. He was finally beginning to think that maybe it had all been in his imagination. That perhaps his mother really had killed his father. That he had just imagined the shadow with the axe, because he didn't want to believe what he had really seen.

After all, that was what the doctors had said.

Then one day a member of the church, Jonathan Peters, was killed in his living room while reading a book.

He had been killed with an axe.

Everything was the same. The man's wife was arrested for murder. Patrick knew the Peters well. He knew the couple loved each other very much. He knew that she did not kill him.

The Peters had a five-year old boy. His name was Eric. Patrick had been his teacher in Sunday school last year. So when he heard the news, he rushed over to the Peters's house.

The police were everywhere. Patrick found Eric lying on the couch. He seemed not to understand what was happening.

"Eric. It's me. Father Gibbons. You have to listen to me. This is very important," Patrick said to Eric.

Eric's eyes were distant, but he nodded.

"Did you see someone with an axe?"

Eric shook his head.

"Did your father have a red book with him last night?"

Eric nodded. Patrick held his breath.

"Where is it now?" he whispered, not wanting the police to hear.

"My room. I found it before I saw daddy..."

"Wait here."

Patrick headed down the hall, making the sign of the cross.

The police were still busy in the living room. No one seemed to have searched Eric's room yet. The room was dark, but the Red Book glowed on Eric's bed. It was the same book he had seen in his father's hands so long before.

"I've finally found you, demon." Patrick whispered and took out a lighter from his pocket. "Now you can go back to hell."

Patrick picked the book up and was about to set it on fire, when he suddenly felt an incredible urge to look inside.

What was it that killed my father?

What could possibly be written in the book of the devil?

He had to know. He had wondered all those years what his father had been reading when he was killed. What had made his father's eyes so dark... and so... so satisfied.

Holding the lighter in one hand, Patrick slowly opened the book. The book instantly opened to the last page.

It said:

Here's what your father saw, Patrick.

"No."

Patrick barely spoke the word before an axe was buried in his back. He fell to the ground, spitting blood from his mouth. He tried desperately to use the lighter, but he had dropped the book on the floor and it had rolled away. The Red Book landed right in front of Eric, who had been standing in the doorway unnoticed. Eric reached down for the book.

"Eric, don't..." Patrick said, his mouth full of blood. But it was too late. Eric had opened the book.

"NO!" Patrick shouted, but nothing happened. Eric flipped(めくる) a few pages, leaned his head to one side, and then brought the book to Patrick.

"I can't read yet," he said.

Patrick thought he heard the agonized(苦痛に満ちた) cry of the demon as he smiled for the last time in his life. Then, he brought the lighter to the book. The book burst into flames.

Father Patrick Gibbons died then, watching the last pages of the book burn to ashes(灰) in front of him.

No one has seen the Red Book ever since.

THE END

A GOOD MAN IS HARD TO FIND

1. Henry Goodman Isn't a Good Man

This is the small town of Everville. It's a middle-class town located on a mountainside. Roughly, eight thousand people live here, work here, study here, and sleep here. Henry Goodman is one of them. His name is Goodman, but he isn't really a good man.

For one thing, he's always been irresponsible. He used to have a wife and a daughter, and a nice place he called home. But Henry liked to gamble. And he gambled a lot. He spent most of his income at a small racetrack in Glassview. He didn't really care if he won or lost. He just liked the excitement.

But his wife cared. And she cared very much.

So one day, his wife took their daughter and left the house. Henry received a letter in the mail a week later, telling him he would never see them again. Henry didn't blame his wife. He'd known it would eventually happen, and he was just glad it was over.

In the days that followed, Henry just woke up, went to work, came home, slept, and went to work again. Sometimes he ate lunch, and sometimes he ate dinner, but rarely^(めったに（食べ）ない) both, and never breakfast. He continued to go to the racetrack once or twice a week, sometimes closing his shop at noon.

2. Henry Goodman Forgets Something Important

Henry's shop was located in the Outside Mall, a worn-out^(ボロボロになった), forgotten shopping center in Old Everville. The only other shop still open at the mall (except for the cafeteria) was some kind of pie or cake shop (he didn't know which, and he didn't care) that some young kid from the city had opened. Heaven-something. Good name, because the mall really needed help from up there.

Several months ago, some guy came to Henry's shop to give him an eviction^(立ち退き通知) notice. The guy said the mall was going to be torn down by that millionaire^(億万長者) in town. The guy also gave Henry another notice to give to the kid next door, but Henry forgot, and after a few weeks, he lost the piece of paper.

At first, he worried about his shop. But after a month of nothing happening, Henry decided it had probably been a mistake, and that everything was going to be okay. So he kept gambling until he lost his house. Even then, Henry wasn't too worried, because he still had his shop, and he could live there. He gambled away what little money he still had.

3. Henry Goodman Loses His Shop

One day, after a morning at the shop that was slow as usual, Henry closed the shop and went to the racetrack. He had an unusually lucky day and won over fifty dollars. He thought his luck was finally changing.

Whistling a tune, Henry went back to the Outside Mall happy and content, until he saw his shop being torn down.

Henry stood there at the bus stop for some time. He spotted the shocked city kid sitting in the ruins of his shop. He suddenly remembered that he had forgotten to give the kid the eviction notice. Henry got scared and ran away.

Henry went to a motel on the outskirts of town to sleep for the night. Unfortunately, the only room available was a family room. Henry rented the room, using up almost all of the money he had won at the racetrack. He realized that he only had five dollars left when he lay down on the bed.

That evening, lying alone in a room with two empty beds, he remembered his wife and daughter, and for the first time, he really understood that he was never, ever going to see them again. It wasn't a joke. Life wasn't a joke. The cold, quiet motel room seemed more real than anything he had ever felt.

He got up and ran away from the motel.

4. Henry Goodman Gets a New Job

Henry took the bus to the New Mall. He didn't have anything else to do. He bought a slice of pizza and ate it while sitting on a bench. It was warm in the mall, and the bench felt good.

Why not just sleep here?

Henry thought this was a good idea until some janitors found him and kicked him out of the mall.

Discouraged, Henry sat down at the front entrance of the mall. Sometime near an hour later, a middle-aged man came running out.

"Did you see someone with a bandage on his head?" the man asked him.

Henry shook his head. The man looked at him suspiciously and asked, "I'm sorry, but why are you sitting here?"

Henry had nothing to lose, so he told the man everything. The man, who turned out to be the owner of the New Mall, was very interested to hear that Henry had been a shop-keeper at the late Outside Mall.

"Maybe this isn't just a coincidence," the owner said. "I think I have good reason to help you."

Henry didn't know what that good reason might be, but he was really grateful when the owner offered him a job as a night maintenance man at the New Mall.

He took the job.

5. Henry Goodman Tries

On that day, something changed inside Henry. A very simple but important dream took hold of him: He wanted to see his wife and daughter just one more time and apologize to them. But before he could do that, he had to prove, to himself, that he could be a better man.

So his days at the racetrack became less and less frequent, and he worked more and more. The job wasn't bad, and the owner was a nice man. For some reason, the owner seemed to trust him, and sometimes he even ran small personal errands for the owner, such as going to Ghost Avenue to buy pies.

He had no idea why the owner wanted pies from a shop in the ghetto. But he did it anyway.

There was one strange thing, though.

Henry had vaguely recognized the man selling the pies. After thinking carefully, he decided it was probably just his imagination.

6. Henry Goodman and the State Pie Festival

All went well until the State Pie Festival.

A week before the festival, the owner had suddenly assigned Henry as the security chief of the festival grounds. He felt incredibly honored by the assignment, but he was also a little scared. Nevertheless, Henry tried his best.

Guarding the Zombie Pies parade was the toughest (もっともきつい) part of the job, but he remembered his daughter had loved that shop, so he was proud to do it.

It was almost the end of the Pie Contest, when it happened. He had been guarding the judges' booth when he saw someone that looked like his wife and daughter walk past him. He rubbed his eyes. It wasn't an illusion (まぼろし). His daughter had grown, but it was her.

He followed after them without thinking much.

Once outside the main tent, his wife turned around and their eyes met. They both froze, but his daughter immediately ran towards him. She cried out, "Daddy!"

He would never forget the moment he hugged (抱きしめる) his daughter for the first time in years. She had gotten so much bigger.

His wife watched in silence as Henry listened to his daughter talk about Zombie Pies. Something about Henry's patience (落ち着き) made her say to him,

"Henry, we moved back to Old Everville last week. There's a room in our house that's empty. If you want to be in our family again, we'll be waiting at the bus stop."

He heard his wife's words but he doubted (疑う) his ears. It was too good to be true. And in a moment of panic, Henry got confused. He wanted to live with them more than anything, but he also thought that he might ruin (だめにする) everything again. So he did the stupidest thing in his life. He ran away.

He knew he would regret (後悔する) it for the rest of his life, but he couldn't stop himself. He ran back to the main tent.

7. Henry Goodman Does It Again

He was sobbing when he got back to the judges' booth. He had just ruined his only chance at happiness. He was so sad, he was sure that this was the lowest point of his life. He was wrong.

Henry glanced inside the judges' booth.

The booth was a complete mess. Someone had destroyed every pie in the booth. The staff and audience were in a huge riot. And it was all his fault. He had left his guard.

Henry saw the crowd shouting at the owner. He had never been more scared in his life. So he did what he had done all his life.

He ran away.

He ran through the crowd, through the festival grounds, and straight through the main gate. He kept running until he was completely out of breath.

8. Way to Go, Henry Goodman!

He finally stopped near the road, feeling terrible and sick of himself. He had done it again. He had disappointed everyone again. He felt that he was the most useless fool in the history of the world.

"Henry, you came," a voice said to him.

Henry looked up and found his wife and daughter standing in front of him.

"I knew you'd come!" His daughter put both arms around him.

Henry stood there bug-eyed. He looked around and saw that he was standing at the bus stop near the mall.

"Here comes the bus," his daughter said, pointing down the road.

His wife told him, "I think you've changed a lot, and I think you deserve a second chance."

Henry still couldn't say anything, but he nodded. The bus arrived and they got on it together. Behind them, the speakers were announcing the rematch at the pie contest, but Henry was so busy hugging his daughter that he didn't hear anything.

Henry Goodman isn't really a good man. But he isn't a bad man either. He doesn't always get the best pie, but still, there are a lot of pies in this world.

A GOOD MAN IS HARD TO FIND

The End

Short Story Collection に関するワンポイント

● **Look & See**
Look & See の文章はタイトルから続けて読むと、「接着剤＋もの」という場所の付録が延々つながっている長い一文になります。このままどこまでもつなげていくことも可能です。英語がうしろへ付録をつなげるだけで、いくらでも文章を作っていける言語であることの、ちょっとおおげさな例としてとらえても楽しいかもしれません。

● **The Last Pages of the Red Book**
気がついていますか？　Red Book の犠牲者には、Father Gibbons も知らない隠された共通点がひとつあることに……。

● **A Good Man Is Hard to Find**
A Good Man Is Hard to Find は Flannery O'Connor の短編小説のタイトルでもあります。ヘンリーの冒険を読み終わったら、もう一度 Big Fat Cat シリーズを読み直してみてください。よく見ると、あちこちにヘンリーの姿が映っているかも……。

BFC BOOKSの終わりに

　ついにここまで来てしまいました。これが Big Fat Cat シリーズ最後のページです。
　エドと猫の物語はこれで終わりです。でも、二人の人生はまだまだ続きます。けれども、それはそっとしておいてあげることにしましょう。
　なぜなら誰の人生もみんな続いていくからです。英語を学ぶことも続いていきます。終わることはありません。この先の道にはこれから出会うたくさんの人々、たくさんの物語が待っています。この物語も、ほかの多くの物語を読み終えた時には、小さな過去の道しるべのひとつとなっていることでしょう。でも、それでいいんです。
　この場所は英語と道を交えた記念の場所です。ひとつの物語を通して、ぼくらスタッフがみなさんとしばしの時を過ごすことができた大事な場所です。でも、ここで立ち止まらずに、どうか先へ進んでください。ぼくらが見えなくなるほど遠くまで、まっすぐそのまま歩いていってください。英語が「できる」ようになった時がゴールではありません。それがスタートです。難しいのはそれからです。せっかく手に入れた便利な道具をどんどん使ってください。
　英語は簡単です。最初からずっとそう言い続けてきました。でも、最後なのでそれに少しだけ付け加えさせてください。英語は簡単です——でも、人に本当の気持ちを伝えるのはどんな言語でも難しいことです。だからこそ、形にこだわらない、心のこもった言葉が必要になります。そのためにどうか、いつまでも英語を好きでいてください。
　もしもいやになったり、つらくなったりしたら、いつでもそっとうしろを振り返ってみてください。その頃にはもう、地平線の彼方に遠ざかっているかもしれませんが、かつて通ってきた道のはるか遠くに、ひょろっとした青年と、大きな太った猫の影が見えるはずです。そしたら、笑顔で思い出してみてください。最初に英語が読めた時の気持ちを。どのくらいうれしかったかを。
　そう。ぼくらはいつまでもそこにいます。
　Good luck and many many happy readings on your journey ahead!

向山貴彦

　当シリーズは英文法の教科書ではなく、あくまで「英語を読む」ことを最大の目的として作られています。そのため、従来の英文法とはいささか異なる解釈を用いている部分があります。これらの相違は英語に取り組み始めたばかりの方にも親しみやすくするため、あえて取り入れたものです。

BFC BOOKS SERIES STAFF

企画・原作・文・解説 向山貴彦	written and directed by **Takahiko Mukoyama**
挿絵・イラスト・キャラクターデザイン たかしまてつを	illustrated by **Tetsuo Takashima**

文章再構成・文章編集・三色辞典編集
吉見知子
story editing and rewriting by
Tomoko Yoshimi

コンテ・アートディレクター
竹村洋司
art direction by
Yoji Takemura

DTP・エディトリアルデザイン・三色辞典編集
中村文
DTP and layouts by
Aya Nakamura

英語アドバイザー・三色辞典編集
井上貴子
reference directed by
Takako Inoue

英文校正
マイクル・キージング
(keezing.communications)
English editing by
Michael Keezing

英語監修
向山淳子(梅光学院大学)
向山義彦(梅光学院大学)
supervised by
Atsuko Mukoyama
Yoshihiko Mukoyama

編集・プロデュース
石原正康
永島賞二
日野淳
edited and produced by
Masayasu Ishihara
Shoji Nagashima
Atsushi Hino

デザイン協力	supportive design by
平川彰	Akira Hirakawa
松田美由紀	Miyuki Matsuda
編集協力	editorial assistance by
井上裕	Yutaka Inoue
武田大作	Daisaku Takeda
宮山香里	Kaori Miyayama

プロダクション・スタッフ	production staff
阿部麻依子	Maiko Abe
須江知子	Tomoko Sue
武口哲也	Tetsuya Takeguchi
西川毅	Tsuyoshi Nishikawa
	and all the other staff of Gentosha
古川俊明	Toshiaki Furukawa
桑田聡子	Satoko Kuwata
北村紀人	Norito Kitamura
製作	
スタジオ・エトセトラ	a studio ET CETERA production
発行	published by
幻冬舎	GENTOSHA

with special thanks to:
井上紬、片岡正明、小山年勇、こやまクリニックのスタッフの皆様、
佐藤祐子、永野文香、梅光学院大学、ブーフーウー、マック＆ジェシー・ゴーハム、みなみ風、
吉見純世、吉見貴子（敬称略）
そして、このシリーズを支えてくださったすべての方々へ

series dedicated to "Fuwa-chan," our one and only special cat

BIG FAT CAT オフィシャルウェブサイト：http://www.studioetcetera.com/bigfatcat
幻冬舎ホームページ：http://www.gentosha.co.jp

〈著者紹介〉
向山貴彦　1970年アメリカ・テキサス州生まれ。作家。製作集団スタジオ・エトセトラを創設。デビュー作『童話物語』(幻冬舎文庫)は、ハイ・ファンタジーの傑作として各紙誌から絶賛された。向山淳子氏、たかしまてつを氏との共著『ビッグ・ファット・キャットの世界一簡単な英語の本』は、英語修得のニュー・スタンダードとして注目を浴び、ミリオンセラーとなった。

たかしまてつを　1967年愛知県生まれ。フリーイラストレーターとして、雑誌等で活躍。1999年イタリアのボローニャ国際絵本原画展入選。著書に『ビッグ・ファット・キャットのグリーティング・カード』(幻冬舎文庫)。

ビッグ・ファット・キャットと雪の夜
2004年12月10日　第1刷発行
2019年 1月31日　第3刷発行

著　者　向山貴彦　たかしまてつを
発行者　見城　徹

発行所　株式会社 幻冬舎
　　　　〒151-0051 東京都渋谷区千駄ヶ谷4-9-7

電話：03(5411)6211(編集)
　　　03(5411)6222(営業)
振替：00120-8-767643
印刷・製本所：株式会社 光邦

検印廃止

万一、落丁乱丁のある場合は送料当社負担でお取替致します。小社宛にお送り下さい。本書の一部あるいは全部を無断で複写複製することは、法律で認められた場合を除き、著作権の侵害となります。定価はカバーに表示してあります。

©TAKAHIKO MUKOYAMA, TETSUO TAKASHIMA, GENTOSHA 2004
Printed in Japan
ISBN 4-344-00717-4 C0095
幻冬舎ホームページアドレス　http://www.gentosha.co.jp/

この本に関するご意見・ご感想をメールでお寄せいただく場合は、comment@gentosha.co.jpまで。

BIG FAT CAT'S
3 COLOR DICTI🐱NARY

**BIG FAT CAT
and the
SNOW OF THE CENTURY**

p.3

1. "...78.8, music in the mountains, Spyglass Radio Network..." 不完全な文
2. "...Hello, all you lonely folks out there listening to the radio on Christmas Day..." 不完全な文

p.4

3. "...Yeah, I know you'd rather be with your family or friends than listening to a DJ on Christmas night — but I'll try my best to keep you from getting lonely. A→B but A→B
"There's a huge cold front coming in directly over the Spyglass area. A＝B
It looks like the weather is going to be really wild tonight. A＝B
— Heck, this might even be the biggest snowstorm of the century! A＝B
"So shut your garage doors and buy plenty of food. (A)→B and (A)→B
It's going to be a long night." A＝B
4. "Meanwhile, here's a good Christmas number... This one's just for you." A＝B... A＝B

p.5

"Oh, darling..." 不完全な文
"Why was I so young... A＝B
So young and so hopeful..." 不完全な文
"Why do my memories come back to me..." A↩
"Oooohhh..." 不完全な文

p.6

"On Christmas Daaay..." 不完全な文
The street corner was a bus stop but someone had stolen all the benches and torn down the roof. A＝B but A→B and (A)→B
The bus stop sign was gone too, so there was no way to know that it was a bus stop. A＝B, so A＝B
5. Even the bus drivers sometimes passed it without stopping. A→B
"Thanks for all the nice presents," BeeJees said to Ed, patting the new knitted cap on his head. A→B
"You really surprised us." A→B
Ed smiled. A↩
He had given presents to almost everyone on Ghost Avenue earlier in the morning. A→B
"You're welcome. A＝B
Sorry, it was all just cheap stuff." A＝B

p.7

6. "Naah, good enough for us." 不完全な文

---

1. 本編 3～6 ページの 1 行目までの文はすべて Spyglass Radio Network（スパイグラス地域のラジオ局）が放送しているクリスマス特別番組の音声です。

2. 番組の DJ がリスナーに呼びかけている部分で、you ＝ lonely folks になります。残りの部分はすべて lonely folks につく化粧品や化粧文です。

3. 日本でクリスマスというとロマンチックなイベントのように思われがちですが、アメリカでは家族と過ごすイメージが強い大切な一日です。感覚的には日本の「お正月」に近いかもしれません。

4. number には「数」のほかに音楽の「曲」を示す意味もあり、ここでは「クリスマス用の曲」という意味で使われています。後半の one は Christmas number の代役です。

5. it は前文の bus stop の代役。

6. Naah は No と同じ意味ですが少し照れているイメージがあります。good enough は本来 It was good enough で「（おれたちには）十分過ぎる」。

7. 英語では「ひざ」を表す言葉は二種類に分かれていて、lap は座った時にできる脚の上の空間、knee は脚が折れ曲がる先端の部分をそれぞれ指しています。

- 1 -

ビッグ・ファット・キャットの三色辞典

7. BeeJees had noticed the one last present on Ed's lap. A→B
8. "Who's present is that? A＝B
    The cat's?" 不完全な文
    Ed took a glance at the red-and-white paper bag on his lap and
        shook his head. A→B and (A)→B
    "No. I already gave the cat a present." 不完全な文 A→B／B'
    Ed pointed at the cat a few feet away. A→B
    "A whole blueberry pie." 不完全な文
    The cat had its head half-buried in a big pie. A→B＝B'
    It noticed and raised its head for a moment, but immediately
        went back to the pie. A↻ and (A)→B, but (A)↻
9. "This one was for Willy," Ed said as he pulled a light pink muffler
        out of the bag. A→B
    "Oh... Yeah," BeeJees nodded. A↻
    They sat in silence for a moment. A↻
    Snow had covered most of Everville before dawn. A→B
    The snow fell at a steady pace throughout the morning. A↻
    Some wind had started to blow, but the weather was
        reasonably calm. A→B, but A＝B
    It was still far from a storm. A＝B
    "Well, don't worry," BeeJees said to Ed. A→B
    "You already gave Willy a much bigger present." A→B／B'

    "Maybe," Ed said, a sad smile on his face. A→B
10. BeeJees couldn't find anything else to say, so he let his eyes
        wander off across the street to the old department store on
        the corner. A→B, so A→B＝B'
11. The building had been closed since the late seventies. A＝B
    The doors were nailed shut, the windows were boarded up, and
        everything else was broken. A＝B, A＝B, and A＝B
    "That store there," BeeJees said abruptly. A→B
12. "It's just a dump now, but you should have seen it when I was a
        kid. A＝B, but A→B
13. Every Sunday, musicians played on that patio. A↻
14. My dad used to take me to see them when he wasn't drunk.
        A→B
15. Me and my baby sister each got an ice cream cone from that
        booth there. A→B
    They had the best strawberry ice cream ever." A→B
    Ed looked at the patio BeeJees was talking about. A→B
16. There were still a few rusty chairs and tables lying around, but it
        was hard to imagine the patio when it was new.
        A＝B, but A＝B

---

p.7

8. この Who's は Who is の略ではなく、「Ed's」「George's」といった時に使われる 's と同じものです。

9. one は present の代役。

10. so 以下の文は、ビージーズが「自分の目を wander させた」と表現することで、自然に道の向こうへ視線が漂っていく感じを出しています。

11. seventies は「(19)70年代」。late をつけることで、70年代の「後半」を指しています。

12. dump はもともと何かを「投げ捨てる」という意味の矢印ですが、それが転じて「ものが投げ捨てられた場所＝ごみため」という役者になっています。

13. patio は中庭にあるテラスのようなところです。

p.8

14. 日本でも「飲む」というと、暗に「お酒を飲む」ことを指しますが、英語でも drink は似たニュアンスを持っています。ここでは drunk の形で、「酔った状態」を指しています。

15. baby sister (brother) は「年下の姉妹 (兄弟)」。子供が自分よりもさらに小さな子供に対して使うことが多い表現です。

16. この hard は「堅い」ではなく「難しい」の意味で使われています。何が「難しい」かというと、to imagine 以下のこと。

Big Fat Cat's 3 Color Dictionary

p.8

It was just like the rest of Ghost Avenue. A = B
A place left behind and forgotten by time. 不完全な文
"Everything seemed to shine in those days." A = B
BeeJees sighed, but with a smile still on his face. A↩

17. "But everything ends, sooner or later. A↩
    Shops close, towns move away... and people... people die.
        A↩, A↩ and A↩
18. That's just the way it is. A = B
19. There's nothing we can do to stop it." A = B

p.9

The snow kept falling without any sound. A→B
It fell on both the rich and the poor. A↩
It fell on all things old and new. A↩
It fell on anything and everything, hiding the world under a soft
    white cover. A↩
"Sometimes," BeeJees said in a sad but gentle tone. A→B
20. "Sometimes, we just have to let go." A→B
    Ed noticed that BeeJees' voice sounded a little bit like Willy's.
        A→B
    It brought him some comfort. A→B／B'
    In a peculiar way, Willy had survived, Ed thought. A→B
    Inside BeeJees. 不完全な文
    Inside himself. 不完全な文
    Inside them all. 不完全な文
21. "Some things, we can't change. But some things, we *can*
        change. You should know," BeeJees said. A→B
    "You taught us." A→B
    Ed nodded. A↩
    After a pause, he said to BeeJees. A↩
    "I'm going to the mall on the two o'clock bus. A = B
22. You know, about the shop in the Food Court." 不完全な文
    "Good idea," BeeJees said, stretching his arms. A→B
    "Hope everything goes really great." (A)→B
    "I'm going to decline the offer." A = B
    "What?" 不完全な文
    "I already have a shop here," Ed said. A→B
    "Besides, they told me I would have to move away from Ghost
        Avenue if I wanted the shop. A→B／B'
    Some rule in the health code, they said. A→B
    And if I rent an apartment, I won't be able to take the cat with
        me." A = B
23. The cat raised an eyebrow. A→B

---

17. 矢印としての end は「終わる」。sooner or later は「遅かれ早かれ」。全体に、なんとなくあきらめた感じの漂う表現です。

18. That は直前のビージーズのセリフを指し、それが世の中の「way（道）」だと言っています。最後の it is は way につく化粧文で「そうあるべき道」。

19. 17 の文の内容を「stop できるものはない」とビージーズが断言しています。

20. let go はよく使われる言い回しで、「（何かを）go させる」、転じて「手を放す、解放する」の意味。ここではビージーズがエドに「手を放さざるを得ない」と語っています。

21. something は「何か」という意味ですが、ここでは Some things と二つの単語に分かれているので、「いくつかのもの」というそのままの意味です。

22. この You know は特に意味のない置き言葉です。「ほら、あれ」という感じで about 以下を強調しています。

23. eyebrow は「まゆ」ですが、猫の「まゆを上げる」仕草ということで、まぶたがぴくっとなった様子を想像してください。

24. **It seemed** to know they were talking about it. **A ＝ B**

    The empty pie plate from the blueberry pie **was** lying at the cat's feet. **A ＝ B**

    24. It と it は両方とも cat の代役です。 **p.9**

25. "Well, **it's** your life." **A ＝ B**

    BeeJees shrugged. **A ↻**

    Ed was about to reply when a voice rang out from above them. **A ＝ B**

    "Yo! **Everything's** ready to go, man!" 不完全な文 **A ＝ B**

    It was George. **A ＝ B**

    He had appeared on the roof of the old department store holding the end of an electric cable. **A ↻**

    The other end of the cable was connected to a telephone pole in the street. **A ＝ B**

    Many of the Ghosts heard George's voice. **A → B**

    They came out from their usual hiding places into the street. **A ↻**

    25. この it は時間などを示す it と同じで、何の代役かは分かりません。「まぁ、おまえの人生だし」とビージーズが少し突き放して言っています。 **p.10**

26. **BeeJees stood** up and **gave** George **a thumbs-up sign**.

    A ↻ and (A) → B／B'

    26. thumbs-up sign は親指を立てて合図をすることで、一般的に「OK」という意味を表します。

27. "Okay, George. **Hit the switch!**" **BeeJees shouted.** **A → B**

    "Gotcha!" **George replied.** **A → B**

    He disappeared behind the edge of the roof. **A ↻**

    The crowd waited in silence. **A ↻**

    Ed stood up too, unable to hide his excitement. **A ↻**

    27. Hit the switch も比較的よく出てくる言い回しで、勢いよく何かのスイッチを入れるイメージのある表現です。

    Another moment passed in the quiet of the snow, and then suddenly, **the roof of the department store lit** up with Christmas lights. **A ↻**, and **A ↻**

    A loud applause rose up from Ghost Avenue. **A ↻**

    Everybody yelled "Merry Christmas!" **A → B**

    George started singing a Christmas tune. **A → B**

    Within seconds, **most of the others joined** in, and **the street became** one big Christmas choir. **A ↻**, and **A ＝ B**

    BeeJees and Ed smiled at each other. **A ↻**

28. "**It's** not anything like the good old days, but it's a lot better than nothing," **BeeJees said.** **A → B**

    The lights were just cheap toy lights bought at the nearest supermarket, and **the electricity was** illegally pulled from the telephone pole, but **the moment was** so wonderful that no one cared. **A ＝ B**, and **A ＝ B**, but **A ＝ B**

    28. 少し抽象的な文です。It は「現在の状況」を指していて、それが「good old days のようではないものの、nothing（何もない）よりはずっとまし」だとビージーズが言っています。 **p.11**

29. After many long years of silence, **Christmas had** finally **returned** to Ghost Avenue. **A ↻**

    29. アメリカでは Christmas という言葉は「愛と希望に満ちた祝福のムード」をもたらす不思議な力を持っています。この日だけは本当に奇跡が起きると信じている人も少なくありません。ここでの Christmas も、どこか「希望（が戻ってきた）」のようなニュアンスを含んでいます。

- 4 -

Big Fat Cat's 3 Color Dictionary

p.11

30. Standing amid the snow, song, and laughter, **BeeJees** *said* once again, softly. A↩

    "Yeah. Some things... you *can* change." 不完全な文 A→B

30. amid は「in the middle of」を縮めた言い方です。

p.14

"Look, cat," Ed *said* to the cat once again. A→B

The cat just *frowned*. A↩

"I *told* you. A→B

You *can't come* with me today." A↩

31. It *was* ten minutes after two o'clock. A＝B

    The bus *had arrived* late. A↩

    Ed *had put* one foot up on the step of the bus. A→B＝B'

    The cat *was* just below Ed, looking up at him with an annoyed expression. A＝B

    It *was* mad because Ed was blocking its rightful path. A＝B

    "You *have* to stay here. A→B

    I'll *be* back soon." A＝B

    The cat *snarled*. A↩

    It *was* tired of Ed blocking its way, so it *decided* to get on the bus. A＝B, so A→B

    "Shut the door! Please!" Ed *yelled* to the bus driver. A→B

    "What?" the bus driver *replied* in a frustrated tone. A→B

    The cat *was* about to jump on the bus. A＝B

    "Shut the door, now!" Ed *repeated*. A→B

31. おなじみの時間の代役 It です。

32. The driver finally *pulled* the door lever, grumbling to himself. A→B

33. The door *slammed* shut just as the cat was getting ready to leap. A↩

    The cat's eyes *widened* as it watched the door close. A↩

    It *became* angry when it saw Ed standing on the other side of the door. A＝B

32. grumble と似た意味の単語で、mumble（ぶつぶつ言う）という言葉もありますが、grumble の方は少し粗暴な感じで、周りに聞こえるようにつぶやいているイメージがあります。それに対して、mumble は聞こえるか聞こえないかくらいの声でつぶやくことを指します。

p.15

The cat *kept* its eyes on Ed as the bus started to drive away. A→B＝B'

Ed *tried* to say something to the cat, but the door *was* too thick. A→B, but A＝B

From inside the bus, Ed *watched* the cat grow smaller and smaller in the distance as the bus hurried down the street. A→B＝B'

The cat *was* still looking at him when the bus rounded a corner several seconds later. A＝B

An absurd question suddenly *popped* into Ed's head. A↩

What if I never see that cat again? A→B

33. slammed shut は「バンと音を立てて閉まった」状態です。leap は「跳ぶ」ですが、jump が一般的に上方向を指しているのに対し、横方向へ跳ぶ場合に使います。

34. He frowned and shook it off immediately.　A↻ and (A)→B
　　Of course I'll see the cat again. Why not?　A→B　不完全な文
　　But all during the bus ride to the New Mall, the image of the cat
　　　sitting there alone on the street came back to him again and
　　　again and never really disappeared.　A↻ and (A)↻

　　The snow was still falling quite lightly when the bus reached the
　　　New Mall some twenty minutes later.　A＝B
　　As the bus crossed the parking lot, Ed could see the empty
　　　space where the Pie Festival had been held.　A→B
　　All the tents and rides were already gone and only a few trailers
　　　and trucks still remained there.　A＝B and A↻
　　Somehow, it all seemed like one big dream now.　A＝B
35. Inside the mall, it was Christmas everywhere.　A＝B
　　A chorus of Christmas songs greeted Ed, and Christmas lights
　　　decorated almost everything in sight.　A→B, and A→B
　　The movie theater near the entrance was showing a romantic
　　　comedy featuring a blue snowman.　A＝B
　　There were a lot of people in front of the theater waiting for the
　　　next showing.　A＝B
36. A child recognized Ed's face and hollered, "Hey! You're that
　　　mustard pie guy!"　A→B and (A)→B
　　The child's parents quickly seized him.　A→B
　　Ed blushed and walked on.　A↻ and (A)↻
　　This happened several more times before he reached the Food
　　　Court.　A↻
　　A giant Christmas tree was standing in the middle of the Food
　　　Court.　A＝B
　　It was decorated with real cookies and candy from stores in the
　　　mall.　A＝B
37. Zombie Pies was doing an "Evil Santa Pie-Fest."　A＝B

　　Ed's feet stopped when he saw the vacant storefront in the Food
　　　Court.　A↻
　　The steel shutters outside the shop were pulled down.　A＝B
　　Ed sat down on a bench in front of the shop.　A↻
38. It was the same bench he had sat on a month before.　A＝B
39. As he looked at the vacant shop, the idea that perhaps
　　　everything had been a dream came back to him again.　A↻
40. This can't be real.　A＝B
41. Maybe I fell asleep on the bench that day, and had a long, long
　　　dream.　A↻, and (A)→B

34. ここで「shook off（振り落とす）」しているのは前文のような absurd question です。

35. 分かりにくいかもしれませんが、この it も時間の代役です。

36. 「大きな声を出す」という時に一番よく使われるのは shout ですが、これは何かを伝えるために大きな声を出すこと。それに「怒りながら叫ぶ」というニュアンスが入ると yell になり、さらに今回のように子供などがあまり意味のないことを大声でわめいている場合には holler を使います。このほかに悲鳴をあげる時に使う scream などもあります。

37. Fest は Festival の略。ジェレミーでなければ考えつかない企画です。

38. a month before で「一カ月前」。the same bench は『Big Fat Cat Goes to Town』21～23 ページでエドが座っていたのと同じベンチだということ。

39. that から dream まではすべて idea の具体的な内容。

40. This は「この状況」を指す代役です。

41. that day は前にこのベンチに座った日を指します。

p.17

Maybe I'm still on that bench...　A＝B
For some reason, the thoughts reminded Ed of the paper inside
　　Willy's fortune cookie.　A→B／B'
42. He dug into his pocket and found it.　A⤴ and (A)→B
43. It still said the same thing.　A→B
44. *Most treasures are in the places you first find them*.　A＝B
　　Ed raised his head to look at the shop again.　A→B
　　Then, he read the words once more.　A→B
　　... in the places you first find them.　不完全な文
　　It was almost as if Willy was congratulating him.　A＝B
45. He knew that wasn't possible, but for a moment, Ed actually
　　believed that it might be.　A→B, but A→B

p.18

"Ed! Ed Wishbone!　不完全な文　不完全な文
I'm so glad you came."　A＝B
Ed's heart skipped a beat when the owner suddenly patted him
　　on the shoulder.　A→B
He was so absorbed in his thoughts that he hadn't realized the
　　owner was standing right beside him.　A＝B that A→B
Ed quickly folded the fortune paper and slid it back into his
　　pocket.　A→B and (A)→B
"Sir. Good afternoon," Ed said, standing up from the bench.
　　A→B
"Did the snow give you any trouble?"　A→B／B'
The owner asked Ed in his usual joyous tone.　A→B
46. "I sure hope not.　A→B
Now come with me and I'll show you your new shop."
　　(A)⤴ and A→B／B'
"Uh... sir, I..."　不完全な文
Ed tried to speak, but the owner went straight to the closed
　　shutters.　A→B, but A⤴
Ed hurried after him, still not sure how to explain.　A⤴
"Just a second, while I open this shutter here..." the owner said,
　　turning a key in the lock.　A→B
"Sir. I'm sorry.　不完全な文　A＝B
47. I have something to..."　A→B
48. Ed felt his stomach tighten.　A→B＝B'
49. He imagined what the owner would say when he told him he
　　didn't want the shop.　A→B
50. But if he was going to say it, now was his only chance.　A＝B
51. "Here we go," the owner said, and threw open the shutters.
　　A→B, and (A)→B

---

42. 前巻の最後で割ったフォーチュン・クッキーの紙をエドはまだ持っていました。そのメッセージに込められた意味とは……？

43. It は paper の代役。said は「（紙が）言っている」＝「書かれている」という意味で使われています。「まだ同じことが書かれている」というと妙なようですが、これは書いてある内容が「同じ意味にしかとれなかった」ことを指しています。

44. them は treasures の代役。you first find them は places の化粧文で「（宝物を）最初に見つけたところ」。

45. 最初の that と後半の it は両方とも前文全体の代役。後半の文は Ed actually believed that it might be possible. を少し省略しています。

46. オーナーは直前の自分のセリフに対して「そうでないことを望む」と言っています。

47. 最後まで言えたなら、B の 箱 の 中 は something to tell you になっていたはずです。

48. 本来 tighten は水道の蛇口などを「きつく締める」時に使う矢印です。ここでは「stomach（おなか）」に使っていますが、エドはおなかが tighten する感覚があるほど緊張しているのでしょう。

49. エドが imagine したのは「"he didn't want the shop" と owner に告げた時、owner が何と言うか」。

The shutters rolled away, revealing an elegant counter with an open kitchen behind it. A↩

The owner turned on the lights and waved his hand towards the inside of the shop. A→B and (A)→B

"Well?" 不完全な文

Ed was speechless. A＝B

His eyes were wide open. A＝B

52. The owner noticed this and smiled. A→B and (A)↩

He grabbed Ed's arm and pulled him inside. A→B and (A)→B

"C'mon inside. (A)↩

Take a look." (A)→B

Ed walked into the shop in a daze. A↩

"Wow..." he whispered. A→B

Everything in the shop looked perfect. A＝B

"The last tenant was a pastry shop. They left everything behind... so you can open your shop at any time," the owner explained. A→B

Ed nodded, but he wasn't really hearing any of the words. A↩, but A＝B

"Is that the kitchen?" Ed asked. A→B

53. "It sure is." A＝(B)

"Can I take a look?" A→B

"Of course you can. A↩

It's your kitchen." A＝B

The owner stepped aside, and Ed moved into the kitchen. A↩, and A↩

Hidden behind the beautiful glass counter were countless pots and pans, kitchen utensils, and spice jars. A＝B

Ed touched the counter. A→B

He stroked its surface softly. A→B

It was smooth and spotless. A＝B

54. "This... is all mine?" A＝B

"Yes," the owner replied. A→B

55. "All you have to do is sign the contract." A＝B

Ed finally recovered his voice, but now, he wasn't sure what to say. A→B, but A＝B

He took a long deep breath and said to the owner, "I have to tell you something." A→B and (A)→B

The owner smiled his jolly smile. A→B

"Sure. Anything." 不完全な文 不完全な文

---

50. it は前文の he didn't want the shop の代役。

51. Here we go はポピュラーな言い回しで、年齢や性別に関係なく、仲間に「さあ、行くぞ」と呼びかける場合に使われます。threw open the shutters は、「シャッターを開いた状態に threw（放り投げる）した」という意味で、この open は「どのように」の付録。

52. this は前文全体の代役。

53. 前文のエドの質問に対する答えです。本来は It sure is the kitchen.

54. This は「ここにあるすべてのもの」のこと。

55. 「エドがしなければならないこと」＝「sign the contract」。

Big Fat Cat's 3 Color Dictionary

p.21

"I..." 不完全な文
I can't accept this prize. A→B
I already have a shop. A→B
Ed tried to say, but the words wouldn't come out. A→B, but A↺

56. The place of his dreams surrounded him in all its hope and splendor. A→B

Ed's voice trembled as he finished the sentence. A↺
"I... uh... thank you. A→B
Thank you for everything." (A)→B
"My pleasure," the owner said, laughing. A→B
"I'm looking forward to having your pie with lunch everyday."
A＝B

The owner handed Ed a contract from his coat pocket and patted him on the shoulder. A→B／B' and (A)→B

57. "Just sign that and bring it to my office before Wednesday.
(A)→B and (A)→B

58. See you then." (A)→B
Ed couldn't help staring at the contract. A→B
When he finally raised his head, the owner was already gone.
A＝B

59. He was there alone with the contract. A＝B
Ed closed his eyes tight. A→B
He hated himself. A→B
He realized he had completely forgotten about Ghost Avenue for the past few minutes. A→B

p.22

60. "So the little youngster wants Evil Santa, huh?" A→B

61. Jeremy stood behind the Zombie Pies counter with red and purple makeup on his face, grinning down at a half-scared, half-happy boy who was waiting for his pie. A↺
"Well, Evil Santa wants you too!" A→B

62. Jeremy suddenly raised his voice and a Santa head with a wicked smile popped up from under the counter.
A→B and A↺
The child and his mother both screamed. A↺
So did Ed. A→B

63. Louder. 不完全な文
"AAAGGGHHHH!" 不完全な文
Jeremy was shaken by the scream. A＝B
He stared at Ed in dumb surprise. A→B
Ed had been watching from behind the mother and child. A＝B
Their eyes met as Ed turned red with embarrassment. A↺

---

56. its は The place of his dreams の代役です。「夢の場所」と言えるほど立派なお店が持っている hope と splendor に囲まれて、エドは断れなくなってしまいます。

57. that も it も contract の代役です。

58. then は「エドが contract を持ってオフィスを訪れる時」です。

59. there は「そこ＝お店の中」の代役ですが、「その場所に（一人で）いる」ことを強調するために入っています。

60. 大人が子供に呼びかける時に使う youngster は「若い」ことを強調した言い方ですが、否定的なニュアンスはほとんどありません。さらに尊敬を持って呼ぶ時には「young man」「young lady」と呼び、逆にけなす時には「kid」「brat」などと言います。

61. 長い文ですが、ほとんどは化粧文です。behind から counter までは「場所」の付録、それ以降は「どのように」の付録です。

62. wicked はもともとは「悪意がある」という意味ですが、ファンタジーや童話などによく使われるため、今では怖いというよりはむしろコミカルなイメージがあります。本当に悪意があることを表現する時には evil を使う方が一般的です。

63. 本来は Ed screamed louder.

64. "Oh, it's you," Jeremy said with a sigh.   A→B
He pulled a rope and the Evil Santa disappeared.
　　A→B and A↩
"*That* was scary," Ed said, slowly recovering from the shock.
　　A→B

65. "If you think that was scary, go use the men's room.
　　(A)↩ (A)→B
You'll be screaming for the rest of the day."   A=B

"Uh... no thank you," Ed said and pointed at the Slime Bucket
　　Pies displayed under the counter glass.   A→B and (A)→B
"But can I get one of those pies?"   A→B
Jeremy frowned but mumbled "Sure," and reached under the
　　counter.   A↩ but (A)→B and (A)→B
He brought out an empty crust shaped like a bowl, and poured
　　a dip of mint slime into the crust.   A→B, and (A)→B
He handed it to Ed with a wooden spoon.   A→B
Ed took a taste and almost immediately said, "This is great!"
　　A→B and (A)→B
Jeremy just shrugged.   A↩

66. "This is the best chocolate mint pie I've ever had," Ed repeated.
　　A→B

67. Jeremy thought Ed was being sarcastic, but Ed really seemed to
　　mean it.   A→B, but A=B

68. *Too bad for Wishbone*, he thought, *because by the time he
　　opens his shop, Zombie Pies will be gone*.   A→B

69. This was his shop's last week.   A=B
Jeremy's father had sold the shop to the Everville Rehabilitation
　　Project.   A→B

70. But he didn't tell this to Ed.   A→B

71. "You are one strange person," Jeremy mumbled, but not in a
　　bad tone.   A→B
"Oh, yeah... do you remember my bodyguard?"   A→B
"Sure," Ed said rather uneasily.   A→B
"Of course."　不完全な文
"He was arrested this morning."   A=B
"He was?"   A=(B)
"The arrest wasn't a surprise.   A=B
He did a lot of *stuff* for my father."   A→B
Jeremy said the word 'stuff' in a disgusted way.   A→B
"The real surprise was that the police were able to catch him.
　　A=B

---

64. it's you は誰か分からない人影が姿を現した時などによく使う言い回しで「なんだ、おまえか」という意味。

65. 一見矢印が二つ並んでいるように見えますが、go and use the men's room が省略されているだけです。「行って○○してこい！」という言い回しの時、強調のために and を消すことがあります。

66. I've ever had は chocolate mint pie の化粧文。

67. it は前文のエドのセリフの代役。mean は「意味する」ですが、ここでは「それを意味している」、転じて「本気で言っている」というニュアンス。

68. Too bad は「悪すぎる」が転じて「残念だったね」という意味になる言い回しです。誰かがささやかな不幸に見舞われた時などにかけるなぐさめの言葉として、よく耳にします。ここで残念なのは because 以下のこと。

69. This は This week の略。

70. こちらの this は前文全体の代役。

71. a strange person とする方がふつうなのですが、one を使うことで「唯一の存在」であることを強調しています。

p.23 72. **He's not** an easy man to catch, you know. A = B
I **think** maybe he wanted to get caught." A→B
"Why?" Ed **asked**. A→B
Jeremy **shrugged** again. A↶

73. He also **knew** that if Billy Bob was caught, his father's arrest was not far away, but **that was** another thing he didn't tell Ed.
A→B, but A = B

p.24 74. "**Beats** me. (A)→B

75. I just **think** so. A→B
He **didn't like** his job very much." A→B
As an afterthought, Jeremy **added**, "He grew up on Ghost Avenue, you know." A→B
Ed **thought** about this for a moment, but **couldn't think** of anything to say. A→B, but (A)→B
"So when are you going to open?" Jeremy **asked**, pretending not to look very interested. A→B
Ed **smiled** awkwardly for a moment. A↶
"I don't deserve that shop," he **said**. A→B
Jeremy **frowned** at Ed while serving another customer a slice of pie. A↶
Ed **said** again, "It's too good for me." A→B
"Yeah, yeah. Of course you don't deserve it. Everyone knows that," Jeremy **said**. A→B
"You only **beat** me and sixteen other bakers! A→B
Sure, you **don't deserve** it!" A→B

76. Ed **realized** what he was saying and **added** in a hurry, "Oh, no no! I **didn't mean** it that way... Sorry. I'm really proud about winning the contest! I really **am**! But that shop... **it's** just way out of my league." A→B and (A)→B

p.25 "I **know**, Wishbone, I **know**." A↶, A↶
Jeremy **seemed** a bit angry, but his voice **was** calm.
A = B, but A = B

77. "So I'll tell you what you don't know," Jeremy **said** as he took the dirty spoon back from Ed. A→B
"The only thing worse than getting a chance you don't deserve, **is** wasting that chance." A = B
Ed **fell** silent. A↶
Jeremy **stuck** his palm out to Ed. A→B

78. Ed **didn't understand** why and just **stared** at Jeremy's palm for a moment. A→B and (A)→B

72. この you know は意味のない置き言葉です。

73. if からカンマまでで「もし〜だったら」。ビリー・ボブが捕まったのなら、自分の父親が逮捕されるのも「far away ではない」とジェレミーは知っています。二つ目の that は前半の文の代役です。

74. Beats me. もともとポピュラーな言い回しです。Beat は「（誰かを）負かす」という意味で、「自分を負かす→降参する」が転じて「分からない」というニュアンスになります。

75. so は「ビリー・ボブは捕まりたかったと思う」というジェレミーのセリフの代役です。

76. この mean も 67 の文と同じで、「そういう意味で言って（いない）」というニュアンスです。セリフの中は色分けすると、I didn't mean it that way... Sorry. I'm really proud about winning the contest! I really am! But that shop... it's just way out of my league.
A→B A = B A = (B)
A = B

77. 少し難しい文です。エドの言い訳に対して「I know」と答えたジェレミーはそれを受けて、「それじゃ、今度はおまえが know していないことを教えてやろう」と言っています。

78. エドが understand できなかったのは Jeremy が palm を突き出した理由です。

- 11 -

"$2.55 for the pie," Jeremy said flatly.   A→B

"Oh... sorry."   不完全な文

79. Ed fumbled in his pocket and pulled out three dollar-bills in a hurry.   A↶ and (A)→B

"Thank you very much."   (A)→B

80. Jeremy took the money and reached under the counter for change.   A→B and (A)→B

"Here's your change," he said and squeezed green slime out from his hand into Ed's palm.   A→B and (A)→B

"AAAAAAGHHHHHH!"   不完全な文

This scream was even louder.   A=B

The six o'clock bus was the last bus, but Ed decided to take the five o'clock bus home.   A=B, but A→B

81. This turned out to be a very good idea, because once the sun set, the snow and wind rapidly grew stronger.
   A↶, because A↶

When Ed got off the bus, the snow on the ground was already up to his ankles.   A=B

82. It was only a short walk back to the theater, but it took him nearly ten minutes to reach the entrance.
   A=B, but A→B／B'

83. "Reporting live from the New Everville Mall, this is Glen Hamperton bringing you coverage of the Christmas celebration events scheduled for tonight."   A=B

The voice from the radio greeted Ed as he closed the door against the snow.   A→B

Ed followed the sound of the radio across the lobby, and into the main theater.   A→B

George was the first one to notice Ed's return.   A=B

"Yo, Ed.   不完全な文

84. You made it just in time, man.   A→B

We were getting kinda worried."   A=B

"Sorry," Ed said as he brushed the snow from his head and shoulders.   A→B

"The snow's getting worse by the minute."   A=B

George, BeeJees, Paddy, Frank, and a few other Ghosts were huddled around the campfire.   A=B

Frank was holding his new radio in his lap with the volume turned up.   A=B

"We were listening to the radio," BeeJees said.   A→B

---

79. fumbled は何かをつかみあぐねて手探りしている様子です。「不器用に扱う」「へまをする」といった意味も持っているので、エドのようなおっちょこちょいには欠かせない矢印です。

80. change は矢印として使われることが多い言葉ですが、ここでは「おつり」という意味の役者です。

81. This は前文全体の代役です。turn out は「結果として○○だと判明する」という意味になる言い回しです。「さんざん turn してやっと out した（外に出た）」というイメージでとらえるとニュアンスがつかみやすいかもしれません。

82. short walk とは「(theater までの) ひと歩き」のこと。二番目の it は short walk の代役で、その「ひと歩き」が実際には何分かかったのかを説明しています。

83. this is（Glen Hamperton）という言い方は、リポーターが中継を始める際の自己紹介などによく用いられます。

84. made it は「それを完成させた」、転じて「成功した」という意味で、この場合は雪がひどくなる前に「到着できた」と言っています。in time は「時間内に (間に合って)」。

Big Fat Cat's 3 Color Dictionary

p.27 85. "**They're** doing live from the mall." A = B

Ed **nodded** and **smiled**. A ↩ and (A) ↩

Glen Hamperton **continued** to talk. A → B

She **was** introducing a local choir group. A = B

George **got** up and **went** to the large, steaming pot that sat
 beside the campfire. A ↩ and (A) ↩

He **grabbed** a tin cup and **dipped** it into the pot.
 A → B and (A) → B

"C'mon, man. We made you some stew," he **said** to Ed. A → B

Ed **sat** down beside BeeJees and **took** the cup from George.
 A ↩ and (A) → B

Warm, homemade stew with large chunks of vegetables.
 不完全な文

It **was** perfect for a day like this. A = B

"So you gave them the bad news?" BeeJees **asked** as Ed sipped
 some stew from the cup. A → B

Ed **paused** for a moment to shake his head. A ↩

86. "I **couldn't**. A → (B / B')

I'm planning to go back tomorrow." A = B

BeeJees **nodded** silently. A ↩

The radio **had started** to broadcast a Christmas chorus. A → B

p.28 87. "Cat, cat, cat. Fat, fat, fat," Frank **sang** along with his own
 words. A → B

88. He **was** singing to a poster he had found somewhere. A = B

"You got the roof repaired in time," Ed **said** to George. A → B

He **realized** that no snow was falling from above. A → B

Several wide planks of wood **had been laid** across the roof,
 covered with some sort of plastic sheet. A = B

89. "Yeah. Paddy helped me," George **answered** proudly, and
 exchanged a high-five with Paddy. A → B, and (A) → B

"Cat fat fat, big fat cat." 不完全な文

Ed **couldn't help** smiling as he listened to Frank's song. A → B

It **was** so peaceful here. A = B

90. He **couldn't believe** that it was just a day ago that Willy had
 passed away. A → B

Ed **knew** that all of them were still sad, but everyone **seemed** to
 just go on with their normal life. A → B, but A = B

91. They **had** all **cried**, they **had** all **said** good-bye, and now, they all
 seemed to know that it was time to move on.
 A ↩, A → B, and, A = B

85. ここでの live は live broadcast の略で、「生中継」という意味です。

86. 本来は I couldn't give them the bad news.

87. his own words は「自分の言葉で」。フランクは自分が作った適当な歌詞で歌っています。

88. he had found somewhere は poster につく化粧文です。

89. high-five とは空中で手のひらをパンと合わせるアクションのことで、仲間同士で「やったぜ！」という気分の時によく行われます。

90. passed away は die よりもソフトな「死」の表現です。「魂が next world へ passed away する」ということです。

91. move だけだと「動く」という意味ですが、move on になると「(off から) on へ動く」という意味合いになり、より前へ進む力が強くなります。この場合も、ウィリーの死によって一時的に off になった人生が「先に進む」時だと言っています。

- 13 -

92. **It seemed** a little **strange** to Ed, who had thought that after someone you loved died, you were supposed to be sad for a period of time.　A＝B

　　At least, **he had been** sad for years, when his mother had passed away.　A＝B

　　— But **he liked** the attitude here better.　A→B

93. For some reason, **it seemed** a lot more natural.　A＝B

　　Some things **we can't change**.　A→B

　　Ed took a sip of stew as he looked over at Willy's stroller sitting alone by the wall.　A→B

　　It would probably **stay** there for a long time to come.　A↺

94. **Ed had asked** the driver of the silent ambulance **where he was taking** Willy.　A→B／B'

95. **The driver had answered**, "I have no idea."　A→B

96. **It had** all **been** sad.　A＝B

97. But sitting there with the Ghosts, in a town that had a very vague sense of time, **it didn't feel** as sad as it had seemed at first.　A↺

98. **It was** just the way it was.　A＝B

　　Ed felt the warmth of the campfire once again.　A→B

　　He felt ashamed of forgetting, even for a short time, **how warm it was here**.　A→B

　　The gentle taste of George's stew.　不完全な文

　　The flickering of the campfire.　不完全な文

　　Frank's funny song.　不完全な文

　　And the slow, almost frozen sense of time inside the theater...
　　　不完全な文

　　Everything he needed was here.　A＝B

　　He shook his head as he finished the stew.　A→B

　　What was he thinking?　A＝B

　　He had to be careful.　A→B

　　He had to think real hard because it was...　A→B

　　Ed suddenly **stood** up in alarm.　A↺

　　His face had become very serious.　A＝B

　　He looked around the theater a second time.　A→B

　　Finding nothing there, **he started** towards the lobby.　A↺

99. "Ed. **What's** the matter?"　不完全な文　A＝B

　　Ed ignored George's question and **rushed** into the lobby.
　　　A→B and (A)↺

　　He came back only a moment later, much more pale than before.
　　　A↺

---

92. It は「ウィリーの死に対する周囲の態度」の代役。a period of time は「（一定の）期間」。

93. it is the attitude here の代役。

94. ambulance が病人やけが人を搬送する時は、サイレンを鳴らしながら走るのがふつうです。それが silent だということは、つまり……。

95. I have no idea. は I don't know. と同じ意味ですが、比較的丁寧な否定の表現です。

96. この It は「ウィリーの死に関するすべて」をひっくるめた It です。

97. この二つの it も前文同様、「ウィリーの死に関するすべて」の代役。in からカンマまでは「時間の感覚がぼやけた町で」という「場所」の付録で、ゴースト・アベニューを指しています。

98. the way it was (is) という表現は本編 8 ページにも出てきています。「それがそれのあるべき道にある」、転じて「あるがままでいい」という意味になります。

99. これも非常によく耳にする言い回しです。「the matter（関心事）は何？」と書いて「どうした？」。

Big Fat Cat's 3 Color Dictionary

p.30

"George," Ed said. A→B
"Where's the cat?" A=B

p.31

100. "Mommy. There was a kitty walking in the snow," the girl said
　　 to her mother from the back seat of her family car. A→B
　　 "What did you say, Jane?" her mother asked from the passenger
　　 seat in front. A→B
101. "I saw a kitty-cat walking in the snow," the girl repeated. A→B
　　 "Don't be silly, Jane. (A)=B
　　 Look at how thick the snow is." (A)→B
　　 "But I know I saw one. A→B
　　 It was a big kitty!" A=B
　　 "It was probably just a fire hydrant or something. A=B
　　 A cat would freeze to death in this weather." A↺
　　 The girl looked outside again. A→B
　　 She knew that her mother was right. A→B
　　 But she also knew for sure that she had seen a big fat cat
　　　　walking along the road. A→B
　　 She had even seen the cat's eyes as it looked back at her. A→B
　　 "I just hope kitty's alright," she whispered. A→B
　　 Only the wind answered, with a high shrill cry. A↺

p.32

"... the storm has now entered the Spyglass district and heavy
　　 snow is falling from the sky. A→B and A=B
　　 The storm is expected to develop into a blizzard soon..." A=B
102. The emergency weather forecast poured out of the radio as Ed,
　　 BeeJees, George, and Paddy gathered in the lobby. A↺
　　 Everyone was covered with snow from head to foot. A=B
103. They looked at each other without hope. A→B
　　 "BeeJees?" Ed asked. A→B
　　 "Nope. Nowhere," BeeJees answered. A→B
　　 "George, did you look around the junkyard?" A→B
　　 "Yeah. It's already covered with snow. 不完全な文 A=B
　　 No footsteps." 不完全な文
　　 A heavy silence filled the lobby. A→B
　　 Only Frank, who seemed not to understand the circumstances,
　　　　kept singing the cat song he had made up. A→B
　　 "The mall," Ed said. A→B
104. "Maybe he came after me." A↺

p.33

105. Ed checked the only working clock in the theater. A→B
　　 "The last bus is due in about five minutes. A=B

---

100. kitty は子猫。

101. kitty に cat をつけて kitty-cat というのは音がかわいいためで、意味は特に変わりません。この呼び方は子猫にも成猫にも使うことがあります。

102. 矢印が poured になっているのはラジオから緊急情報が「あふれ出す」ように次々と流れてくる様子を表現するためです。

103. They はそこにいる全員の代役です。

104. 今まで猫のことを it と表現してきたエドですが、緊急事態のためかとっさに「he」と呼んでいます。英語では動物に対する代役として、it も、he も、she も使うことができます。逆にどれを選択するかで、その動物に対する気持ちが読み取れることもあります。ここでのエドはおそらく猫の性別をはっきりとは知らずに、イメージで選んでいるのでしょう。

105. work は「働く」ですが、この場合は「正常に動作している」ことを指しています。theater 内でまともに動いている時計が一つしかないのですから、時間の感覚があいまいになるのも当然かもしれません。

ビッグ・ファット・キャットの三色辞典

p.33

I **have** to go." A→B
106. George and Paddy **looked** at each other, then **grabbed** hold of
   Ed's arms so he **couldn't run** off. A→B, then (A)→B so A◯

"Ed, man! Wait a minute," BeeJees **said**. A→B
"I **have** to find the cat! A→B
He**'ll freeze** to death in this weather!" A↩
"You'll freeze to death first!" BeeJees **shouted**. A→B
"If you take the last bus to the mall, how **are** you going to get
   back? A=B
You sure as hell **can't** *walk* in this weather!" A↩
Ed **wasn't** listening. A=B
Paddy **held** Ed tighter, thinking he was going to run towards the
   door, but Ed **was** staring at something else. A→B, but A=B
"Frank," Ed **said**, blinking his eyes. A→B

106. 真ん中の文の矢印は grabbed です。その直後の hold は「握ることのできる場所」という役者で、矢印ではありません。

107. "Frank?" BeeJees **asked** with a puzzled look. A→B
They all **followed** Ed's eyes to Frank. A→B
Frank **was** still singing his cat song to the poster he held. A=B
Ed **loosened** George and Paddy's grips and **walked** over to
   Frank. A→B and (A)↩
"Frank." 不完全な文
Ed **started** to reach for the poster Frank was holding. A→B
"Where **did** you **get** this?" A→B

107. puzzled は「困惑した」という意味の化粧品です。この単語を役者として使うと puzzle「パズル」になります。

"Outside," Frank **replied** with a smile. A→B
108. "Good man **give** me." A→B
"Today?" Ed **asked** again. A→B
109. "Uh-huh." 不完全な文
Frank **pointed** happily at the poster. A→B
"Cat!" 不完全な文
BeeJees and George **came** beside Ed and **took** a look at the
   poster. A↩ and (A)→B
110. They **held** their breath. A→B
"Oh no..." Ed **whispered**. A→B
Ed **grabbed** the poster. A→B
As soon as he read the first two lines, he **headed** for the door.
   A↩
George and BeeJees **ran** after Ed and **seized** him just as he was
   about to step outside. A↩ and (A)→B
"Let me go! (A)→B=B'
I **have** to go! A→B
He's my cat!" A=B
"Ed!" BeeJees **said** to him in a desperate tone grabbing him by
   the collar. A→B

p.34

108. フランクのセリフなのでちょっとおかしな文になっていますが、正しくは A good man gave me (the poster).

109. Uh-huh というのは「うん、うん」とうなずく時の言葉で、小さな子供などがよく使います。

110. held their breath は「息をつかむ」、転じて「息を止める」という意味になります。held という単語には「がっちりつかむ」イメージがあるので、息詰まる瞬間などを表現する時によく用いられます。

p.34
The weather outside was really dangerous. A = B
BeeJees knew he had to stop him. A → B
He shouted in Ed's face, "ED!" A → B
Ed stopped struggling. A → B
His face was frozen with fear. A = B

111. BeeJees spoke as calmly as he could, "Ed. Listen. Do you really think that anyone can catch that cat? I think... maybe the cat *knew*." A → B

111. ここではビージーズは猫が何を知っていたかについては触れていません。その内容は4文先で出てきますが、エドは何のことかぴんと来たようです。

p.35
Ed's face grew stern as he heard those words. A ↻

112. "I know it sounds crazy! A → B
But... but maybe... 不完全な文
Maybe the cat knew that you couldn't take him with you. A → B
Maybe he left because he wanted you to have that shop in the mall!" A ↻ because A → B = B'
Ed lowered his arms. A → B

113. BeeJees let go. A → B
Ed staggered back a step, not saying a word. A ↻
He had forgotten about the cat. A → B

114. He was so selfish that he had forgotten all about the cat. A = B
He looked around the lobby at everyone's worried faces, then closed his eyes. A → B, then (A) → B
"Damn!" 不完全な文
Ed hit his hand hard on the ruins of the ticket counter. A → B
"What am I doing? *What am I doing!*" he shouted. A → B
Full of anger at himself, Ed reached into his pocket, took out the contract from the New Mall, and ripped it into shreds.
A → B, (A) → B, and (A) → B
He threw the pieces on the floor. A → B

115. "I'm sorry," Ed said. A → B
And before anybody could move, Ed shoved George back with both hands and ran through the door. A → B and (A) ↻

p.36
116. "Ed!" BeeJees shouted after Ed, but George bumped into him and they both fell down.
A → B, but A ↻ and A ↻
When they finally got back to their feet, Ed had already disappeared into the snow. A ↻
George and BeeJees stood at the front door of the theater, helplessly looking out into the snowstorm. A ↻

117. The snow was no longer a romantic ornament for the streets.
A = B

112. it は前のビージーズのセリフ全体の代役。

113. let go は「行かせる→自由にする」。ここでビージーズが let go したのはエド。

114. 日本語で selfish に近いのは「わがまま」とか「自分勝手」ですが、英語の selfish はそこにさらに「卑怯」なイメージが加わり、いっそう印象の悪い言葉になっています。

115. 何に対して sorry なのかは次の文で明らかになります。

116. bumped は「ドンとぶつかる」という意味ですが、crashed などと比べると、少しやわらかいぶつかり方です。車が crashed したら中の人は即死しているイメージがありますが、bumped の場合はけがをしているかどうかという程度です。

117. no longer は、これまで streets のロマンチックな装飾品だった雪が、「もはやそうではなくなった」という意味。

118. **It was** now a dangerous enemy.　A＝B

Behind them, Frank's radio **continued** to give the weather forecast in a flat, emotionless tone.　A→B

119. "...**the wind has** now **reached** forty miles per hour **and it is** very **dangerous to walk outside**..."　A→B and A＝B

A half hour later, Ed **arrived** at the New Mall and **went** straight to the pay phone near the entrance.　A↶ and (A)↶

He **found** the number of the Everville Health Center on the poster and **dialed** it.　A→B and (A)→B

After the tenth ring, a man's voice finally **answered**.　A↶

The man **seemed** tired and reluctant to talk.　A＝B

Ed hurriedly **explained** what had happened.　A→B

"Yes. Big, dark, mean... It's usually walking around Ghost Avenue. Yes! Yes! That's my cat," Ed **cried** into the phone excitedly.　A→B

"**Have** you **caught** him?"　A→B

The passing customers all **stared** at Ed with suspicious looks on their faces.　A→B

Ed **lowered** his voice a little.　A→B

"Yes... near Ghost Avenue... Yes... and did you... You chased him for four blocks!?" Ed **shouted** into the phone.　A→B

He **lowered** his voice again after a few middle-aged women pointed at him.　A→B

"But... but he **escaped**?"　A↶

Half relieved and half disappointed, Ed **took** a deep breath.　A→B

120. **The man on the other end seemed** outraged.　A＝B

"Yes... yes.　不完全な文

Sir, **I'm** really **sorry** the cat ripped your new jacket... yes, and your new pants... and of course, sir, **I'll be** glad **to pay for the belt** too, but **could** you please **tell** me where you saw him last?　A＝B, A＝B, but A→B／B'

Sir? Sir? Please **don't hang** up!"　不完全な文　不完全な文　(A)↶

But the man **hung** up.　A↶

Ed **put** the phone back down on the hook.　A→B

121. He **turned** from the phone, and almost **walked** straight into Jeremy, who was standing behind him.　A↶, and (A)↶

122. Jeremy **was dressed** to leave work.　A＝B

He **had** a cell phone in his hand.　A→B

"I thought you already went home," Jeremy **said**, adding in a sarcastic tone, "Or at least something like a home."　A→B

---

118. It は snow の代役。

119. forty miles per hour は風速を表しています。日本の単位に直すと、風速約 64 キロメートル。it は同じ文の最後にある to 以下の代役。

120. the other end は「（電話線の）もう一方の端」のことで、電話の向こう側にいる相手を指しています。

121. who 以下は Jeremy につく化粧文。

122. to 以下は dressed を具体的に説明している部分です。ゾンビ・パイズで働いている時のジェレミーの扮装を思い浮かべると、仕事を終えて帰るところなのがよく分かります。

p.38

Ed stared at Jeremy for a moment. A→B
Then he showed him the poster. A→B／B'
"My cat's lost." A＝B
Jeremy looked at the poster without much thought. A→B
As he read the lines, his frown grew deeper, and finally froze
  into an expression of horror. A↺, and (A)↺
He spoke to Ed in a low voice. A↺
"Wishbone. 不完全な文
123. This isn't good news. A＝B
You could be disqualified for this." A＝B
"I don't care." A↺
124. "Of course you do!" A↺
125. This might be your only real chance in life and you..." A＝B

p.39

Jeremy realized that Ed wasn't looking at him. A→B
126. His eyes were glued to a small crowd that was developing at the
  center of the mall. A＝B
The reporter, Glen Hamperton, was in the middle of the crowd
  with a microphone in one hand. A＝B
127. There were also several television cameras moving among the
  crowd. A＝B
128. It was probably the program George and BeeJees had been
  listening to on the radio. A＝B
"Wishbone! Listen to me!" 不完全な文 (A)↺
Jeremy grabbed Ed to make him look his way. A→B
129. Ed did, but his eyes didn't stop on Jeremy's face. A↺, but A↺
130. They stopped on the cell phone he was holding. A↺
131. An idea had come to his mind. A↺
"Wishbone! I said..." 不完全な文 A→(B)
"I have to borrow this," Ed said, and without waiting for an
  answer, took the phone from Jeremy's hand. A→B, (A)→B
Jeremy opened his mouth wide in annoyance as he watched Ed
  examine the phone. A→B
132. "Is this the number for the phone?" A＝B
Ed asked Jeremy, showing him the phone number taped on the
  side with cellophane tape. A→B
"Yes. I have so many phones that..." 不完全な文 A→B
"Thanks," Ed said and ran off towards the crowd of people.
  A→B and (A)↺
"Wishbone! Hey, wait a minute! 不完全な文 (A)↺
133. Damn it!" (A)→B

123. This は poster に書いてある内容。

124. 本来なら Of course you do care! で「気にするべきだぞ！」。

125. This は「パイ・コンテストに勝ったこと」。

126. His eyes とはエドの eyes のこと。

127. 同じ「〜の間」という意味の言葉でも、between は二つのものの間を行ったり来たりしている様子を表し、among は三つ以上のものの間を動き回る様子を指します。

128. It は「モールの中央で行われているイベント」の代役。

129. 最初の文は本来 Ed did look his (Jeremy's) way. で、前文を受けてエドがジェレミーに視線を向けた様子を表しています。

130. They は his (Ed's) eyes の代役で、he は Jeremy の代役。

131. ふつうなら「エドが idea を思いついた」とするべき文ですが、逆に idea の方から「やって来た」と表現することで、ある考えが突然頭に浮かぶ感じを伝えています。

132. this は次の文の the phone number taped on the side with cellophane tape の代役。ビジネスマンのジェレミーは、たくさん持っている携帯電話の番号をいちいち覚えていられないのでしょう。

134. **It took** another moment for Jeremy to sigh and run after Ed. 　A→B

By the time Jeremy arrived at the edge of the crowd, **Ed was squeezing** between people, trying to get to the stage in the middle. 　A＝B

Jeremy bit on his lower lip. 　A→B

"Wishbone... What the hell **are** you **doing**?" 　不完全な文　A＝B

135. **Jeremy followed** after Ed but **was blocked** by a group of teenagers who wanted to shake his hand. 　A↩ but（A）＝B

Jeremy fought them off, but by the time he escaped, **Ed had** already **climbed** onto the stage. 　A→B, but A↩

Guards came forward to stop him, but **Glen Hamperton recognized Ed** immediately. 　A↩, but A→B

136. "**Look** who we have here, everyone! 　（A）→B

The winner of the state pie contest, Ed Wishbone!" 　不完全な文

The crowd cheered, thinking Ed was a guest on the show. 　A↩

Ed ignored them and **went** straight towards Glen.
　A→B and（A）↩

"Well, what **brings** you here today, Ed?" 　A→B

Glen pointed the microphone towards Ed. 　A→B

"I'm sorry," **was** all **Ed said** before he took the microphone from Glen's hand. 　A＝B

Glen stared in pure surprise as Ed stepped in front of her to face directly into the camera. 　A↩

137. "I'm sorry to interrupt. But this is something very important to me," **Ed said**, his voice shaking with urgency. 　A→B

The crowd around the stage **heard** the serious tone in his voice.
　A→B

The cheering and shouting **died** down. 　A↩

Ed took a deep breath and **held** the poster up to the camera.
　A→B and（A）→B

"My cat is lost in the snow somewhere," **he said** as the camera focused on the poster. 　A→B

"I **need** your help. Everyone's help." 　A→B　不完全な文

In that one moment, **the picture** of the cat **was broadcast** to every house in Everville. 　A＝B

138. **Snowed-in families** sitting in their living rooms watching television all **moved** closer to the screen to get a better look.
　A↩

The owner of the New Mall **happened** to be watching television in his office with a beer in hand. 　A→B

ビッグ・ファット・キャットの三色辞典

p.40

133. Damn it は「ちくしょう」という意味の言い回しです。

134. It は to sigh 以下の代役です。

135. who wanted to shake his hand は teenagers につく化粧文。

136. 「私たちがここに持っている誰か」と書いて「誰がここに来てくれたのか」。思いがけないエドの登場にリポーターも驚いているようです。

p.41

137. this は「これから話すことになる内容」の代役。

138. Snowed-in とは「雪によって（中へ）閉じ込められた」という化粧品。

p.41

He sprayed his beer all over his desk when he saw the poster.
A→B

139. Jeremy covered his eyes with his right hand and moaned.
A→B and (A)↩

On Ghost Avenue, George, Paddy, and BeeJees all crowded around the radio unable to believe what they were hearing.
A↩

BeeJees dropped his mug on the ground and whispered, "Oh, shit." A→B and (A)→B

p.42

"If you have seen this cat, please call me at 555-22xx. (A)→B

140. This is the cat that ruined the first round of the pie contest yesterday. A=B

The health center is chasing him. A=B

141. I didn't know any of this until today. A→B

I'm really sorry, and I'm fully responsible for the situation.
A=B, and A=B

I'll give back all my prize money and disclaim ownership of the shop in the New Mall as soon as possible."
A→B and (A)→B

Ed looked straight into the camera and said to the people of Everville. A↩ and (A)↩

"But right now, I have to find my cat. A→B

142. That's all that matters." A=B

A silence followed as Ed stared into the camera for a moment.
A↩

Nobody in the crowd moved. A↩

p.43

After taking a deep breath, Ed gave the microphone back to Glen and stepped off the stage. A→B and (A)↩

The crowd remained frozen in position. A↩

Ed was sure that everyone was angry at him. A=B

He didn't look up. A↩

But after a moment, a woman began clapping her hands. A→B

Then a man joined in. A↩

A brief pause followed, and then, several other people started clapping their hands. A↩, and A→B

Ed looked around. A↩

He was so dumbfounded that he bumped into a bleak-faced Jeremy as he stepped out of the crowd. A=B

"What the hell was that?" Jeremy asked in an angry voice.
A→B

---

139. moaned はつらいことや痛いことがあった時に「うなり声を上げる」こと。

141. this は「猫がパイ・コンテストの first round をだめにしたこと」の代役。

142. That は前文全体の代役。matters は「（エドにとって）関心のある」。all that matters で「関心のあるすべてのこと」、つまり「それ以外はどうでもいい」と言っています。

"I need to borrow your phone for a while," Ed said. A→B

"Forget the phone, you idiot! (A)→B

Do you know what you've done? A→B

You just threw away the best chance of your life!" A→B

143. Ed gave him one short nod and headed down the aisle.

 A→B／B' and (A)↩

 Jeremy followed along, shouting at him. A↩

144. "What stupid reason was that for? A＝B

 The cat doesn't even have a collar! A→B

 Anybody would have thought it was a stray! A＝B

 Why did you have to say on TV that it was your cat?" A→B

 Ed didn't slow down for a second. A↩

 He was headed straight outside. A＝B

 Jeremy sighed, shook his head, and with a slight change of tone in his voice, continued shouting at Ed.

  A↩, (A)→B, and (A)→B

 "And what are you going to do without a car? A＝B

 Walk!? 不完全な文

145. It's nine degrees below zero outside, you nitwit!" A＝B

 Ed finally came to a stop by the exit. A↩

 The snow had become even fiercer in the last few minutes.

  A＝B

146. The weather outside was so violent that even Ed, despite his determination, had to stop for a moment. A＝B

147. "You're really going to choose a cat over a shop in the mall?"

 Jeremy asked Ed one last time. A→B／B'

 "The cat... he chose me," Ed replied. A→B

148. "You're so damn stupid, it's almost illegal," Jeremy said, as he pulled out his car keys and headed for the door. A→B

 "You wait here." A↩

 When Jeremy opened the door, the snowstorm noticed, and attacked full force. A↩, and (A)↩

149. Jeremy winced, but stood his ground. A↩, but (A)→B

150. The last thing he did before stepping out into the snow was to say to Ed, A＝B

151. "And you better check on that 'he' part." A→B

 Ed watched in surprise, as Jeremy dashed through the snow to his car. A↩

 He wanted to thank him, but he had no time to do that now.

  A→B, but A→B

---

143. one short nod というのは小さく一回うなずくことです。 p.43

144. that はエドがテレビに向かって行ったパフォーマンス全体を指し、「(あんなことをした) stupid reason は何だ」とジェレミーが問いただしています。 p.44

145. It は天候の代役。nitwit は「バカ」というのを比較的おだやかに表現した言葉です。nit は「シラミ」、wit は「知恵」で、「シラミ並みの知恵しかない」というたとえが元になってます。

146. despite his determination はとばして読むことも可能です。

147. choose ○○ over ××という表現は、○○を××よりも優先して選択する場合に使います。ここでも cat を shop in the mall より上（over）に持ってくることで、そちらを選ぶことを示しています。

148. エドのお人よしぶりにあきれかえったジェレミーが、「それだけバカだとほとんど違法だ」ときつく言い放っています。 p.45

149. stood his ground は「自分の地面を保った」、転じて「ふんばった」。

150. A の箱の中の he 以下はすべて last thing につく化粧文です。

151. エドが猫を he と呼んでいるのを聞いて、この種のことに苦い経験のあるジェレミー（『Big Fat Cat and the Fortune Cookie』参照）は気になったのでしょう。

Big Fat Cat's 3 Color Dictionary

p.45 The snowstorm had arrived. A↩

p.46 152. "Okay folks, I have a message here from one of our listeners."
A→B
"Hello, SRN. 不完全な文

153. I'm a college student visiting my grandparents in Everville for winter vacation. A＝B

154. It's been a great Christmas for me. A＝B

155. All the family together, delicious homemade dinners, watching a lot of old movies, a warm fireplace, and a whole bunch of presents!" 不完全な文

p.47 "I have to tell you... Christmas is the best time of year."
A→B... A＝B

p.48 156. Jeremy's black limousine fought through the snow, swerving and sliding, as they drove south on Valley Mills Drive. A↩
The car routinely skidded sideways off the road, flinging Ed across the back seat countless times. A↩
He sat up quickly but was soon flung again, and each time he banged his head into something hard.
A↩ but (A)＝B, and A→B
"Please keep the car steady!" (A)→B＝B'
Ed cried to Jeremy from the back seat after a fifth encounter with the back door. A↩

157. Jeremy, driving with almost zero visibility, shouted back angrily. A↩

158. "It would help if you closed the damn window! A↩
We're going to catch pneumonia!" A＝B
Snow was blowing in through the back window. A＝B

159. Driving the limousine was even more difficult with snow swirling not only outside, but inside the car too. A＝B
Ed kept his eyes on the roadside with his head poking halfway out the window. A→B＝B'

160. But it was impossible to spot a single cat in this snow. A＝B

161. Ed's lips had gone from blue to black, and he could barely keep his eyes open in the cold wind. A↩, and A→B＝B'
Hope ran out of him with every passing second. A↩
Jeremy took a glance at Ed and saw the desperate look on his face. A→B and (A)→B
He swallowed once. A↩

---

152. 本編46〜47ページの見開きに出てくるセリフはすべてSRN（Spyglass Radio Network の略）のラジオ番組で流れている音声です。

153. Bの箱の中のvisiting 以下は、すべて college student につく化粧文。

154. It は時間の代役。Today に置き換えると分かりやすくなります。

155. 154 の great Christmas の理由を次々にあげています。暖炉の前でおだやかに過ごす、幸せな家族の様子が浮かんできます。

156. swerving and sliding は fought を具体的に説明している付録です。

157. zero visibility で「視界ゼロ」。ジェレミーはほとんど外が見えない状態で運転していることが分かります。

158. It は if 以下の行為の代役で、「窓を閉めてくれたら助けになるぞ」。

159. not only 以下は snow がどこで swirling しているかを具体的に説明しています。大雪の中で窓を開けていたら、こうなるのは当然です。

160. it は to spot 以下の代役。a single cat は「たった一匹の猫」という感じで、大雪の中の猫がいかに小さな存在かを強調しています。

162. "Look, I don't want to sound cruel, but I'm sure you've realized by now that if the cat were still outside, it would already be dead." A→B, but A＝B

Jeremy took another look in the rearview mirror. A→B
Ed seemed not to have heard what Jeremy had said. A＝B
"Wishbone! 不完全な文
163. Are you listening, dammit? A＝B
We could easily die out here too, you know!" A↺
Ed bit on his lower lip. A→B
The big roadside sign for the New Mall stood on the other side of the road. A↺
Everything beneath it was already buried in the snow. A＝B
He knew Jeremy was right. A→B
They could have passed the cat anywhere. A→B
164. His mind told him it was pointless. A→B／B'
But the image of the cat sitting there on the street earlier today, and the image of that same cat lying beneath cold snow, slowly freezing to death, wouldn't allow Ed to give up. A→B＝B'
Some things you can change. A→B
165. He had to believe. A→B
He was so damn tired of losing everything. A＝B

Jeremy's cell phone suddenly rang. A↺
166. Ed fumbled for the phone. A↺
It took him a moment to press the talk button with his cold fingers. A→B／B'
167. It was a short but horrible moment for Ed. A＝B
He was scared that the caller might hang up. A＝B
"It's probably just another crank call," Jeremy muttered. A→B
"Hello?" Ed said into the phone. A→B
"Hello?" 不完全な文
There was some background noise, but no voice at the other end. A＝B
It seemed like another hoax. A＝B
There had been five of them already. A＝B
But this time, after a long pause, a small girl's voice came from the speaker. A↺
"I saw your kitty," the girl said. A→B
"It was walking down Valley Mills Drive. A＝B
Near the big sign for the mall." 不完全な文

---

p.49

161. 「唇が青から黒に行ってしまった」というと分かりにくいですが、gone を changed にしてみると意味がつかみやすくなります。ここで gone が使われているのは、「変わってしまった」という否定的な変化を表現するためです。

162. you've 以下を色分けするとこうなります。 you've realized by now that if the cat were still outside, it would already be dead. A→B

163. dammit は damn it を省略したもので、「くそっ」と吐き捨てるような響きがあります。

164. it は「猫を探すこと」の代役。

165. believe しなければならないのは前文全体の内容です。

p.50

166. 79 の文にもありますが、ここでもあわてたエドがポケットの中の携帯電話を fumbled しています。分かりにくければ、the phone をBの箱に入れて考えてもかまいません。

167. It は前文の a moment to press the talk button with his cold fingers の代役。その瞬間はエドにとって「short だが horrible」なものでした。

"Valley Mills Drive? Here!?" Ed repeated.   A→B
They had just passed that 'big sign' moments ago.   A→B

168. "Could you tell me when...?"   A→B／B'
But the phone was already dead.   A=B
The child had hung up, perhaps she was too shy or scared to talk anymore.   A↩, A=B
"Thank you," Ed said softly into the phone and rushed to the window once again.   A→B and (A)↩
He said to Jeremy, "A girl called. She said she saw my cat somewhere near here!"   A→B

169. "And of course you believe her," Jeremy said in a sarcastic tone.   A→B

170. Ed went back and forth across the car trying to spot something — any sign of the cat.   A↩
Jeremy opened his window too.   A→B
The snow flew through the car now, making the inside of the car almost the same as the outside.   A↩
They looked and looked, but all they could see was white land.   A↩ and (A)↩, but A=B

171. Ed spotted the sign for the sandwich shop he had stopped at.   A→B
He could almost see a phantom image of himself and the cat on the roadside, still looking for a new job.   A→B

172. Everything that had happened since then — both the good and the bad — the cat had always been there with him.   A=B
The image of the cat lying dead in the snow rose up in his mind again, and he closed his eyes to fight the tears.   A↩, and A→B
"Willy..." Ed said, almost like a prayer.   A→B

173. It was the only word he knew that seemed stronger than the despair outside.   A=B

174. And that very name brought something back into his mind.   A→B
The fortune paper.   不完全な文
Something told him to take the paper out of his pocket and read it one final time.   A→B=B'

175. So he did that.   A→B
Most treasures are in the places you first find them.   A=B

176. And this time, the words made perfect sense.   A→B
Ed jumped to the window again and stuck his head out as far as he could.   A↩ and (A)→B

168. when...のあとに省略されているのはthis happened。

169. 今までさんざんエドの常識はずれた人のよさに驚かされてきたジェレミーは、小さな女の子からのあいまいな情報でさえ「もちろんおまえは信じるわけだな」と皮肉を言っています。

170. 先ほどは「看板」として出てきたsignですが、ここでは「印」という意味です。

171. エドが『Big Fat Cat Goes to Town』で昼食を買うために立ち寄ったsandwich shopのことです。

172. thenは「猫と一緒にこの道を歩いた時」の代役。最後のwith himは「彼と共に」。

173. Itは前文のエドのセリフの代役。

174. that very nameのveryは「まさに(その名前)」。

175. thatは前文のB'の箱の中全体の代役。

176. made senseは言い回しで、「意味をなす」ことを表します。

The snow **attacked** him fiercely, but about a hundred feet ahead,
he **was** able to see the road fork towards Old Everville —
towards the Outside Mall.　A→B, but A＝B

177. *It wasn't about the shop*, Ed **thought**.　A→B

178. *It* **never** *was*.　A＝(B)

"**Turn** left at the next corner!" Ed **said** to Jeremy.　A→B

"What!?"　不完全な文

Jeremy **thought** he'd heard wrong.　A→B

The road to the left at the traffic signal **was** very narrow and
was already deeply **covered** in snow.　A＝B and (A)＝B

It **wasn't** even a road anymore.　A＝B

It **was** just a pile of snow.　A＝B

"**I need** to get to the Outside Mall.　A→B

Turn left at that corner.　(A) ↻

179. **It's** over the hill."　A＝B

"That corner?" Jeremy **shouted**, pointing at the nonexistent
road ahead.　A→B

"*That corner!?*"　不完全な文

You're insane!　A＝B

We'll **get** stranded and **die**!"　A→B and (A) ↻

Ed **took** a deep breath and calmly **said**, "Then let me off at the
corner."　A→B and (A)→B

"You're kidding."　A＝B

"I'm **not**.　A＝(B)

180. **Pull** over by the side and **I'll get** off."　(A) ↻ and A→B

The corner **was approaching** fast.　A＝B

A precious moment **passed** before Jeremy was able to say
anything.　A↻

"Now, **wait** a minute.　(A) ↻

181. Let's **consider** this again.　(A)→B

You **want** me to drive this extra fancy limo *into that pool of
snow*?!"　A→B＝B'

The corner **was** now moments away.　A＝B

Jeremy **caught** a glimpse of Ed getting ready to go out into the
snow and **spoke** faster.　A→B and (A) ↻

"**Do** you **know** what this car cost?!　A→B

The front bumper probably **cost** more than everything in your
bank account!　A→B

And **look**!　(A) ↻

This new audio system **cost** something like... damn!　A→B

---

p.53

177. It は fortune paper に書かれていた内容の代役で、それが「shop のことじゃなかったんだ」とエドは考えています。

178. 分かりやすく書き直すなら、The words of the fortune paper never was about the shop.

p.54

179. It は Outside Mall の代役。

180. 省略されていますが、本来は Pull over the car by the side of the road. で「車を道の脇によせる」ことを意味しています。

181. this は次文全体の代役。信じられないエドの提案に、ジェレミーもこう言わざるを得ませんでした。

p.55

p.55 182. **TO HELL WITH IT!** 不完全な文
I'M RICH ANYWAY!" A＝B

183. Jeremy **yanked** the steering wheel to the left and the car **spun** off towards Old Everville, crashing head first into the heavy drift.   A→B and A↻

p.56 "And now the road down to Standpoint **is** completely **cut** off."   A＝B

All public transportation in the Spyglass area **has been** halted.   A＝B

Please **remain** indoors until further notice..."   (A)↻

Frank's radio **kept** repeating the same message over and over.   A→B

BeeJees, George, and Paddy all **sat** around the fire, looking glumly at the radio.   A↻

184. The wind **shook** the old theater to its foundations, reminding them how dangerous it was outside.   A→B

BeeJees **sighed**.   A↻

"There's no way the cat could still be alive."   A＝B

No one **answered**.   A↻

George and Paddy **tended** the fire in sad silence.   A→B

BeeJees **stared** at the floor.   A→B

185. **"Uh-uh,"** someone **said**.   A→B

BeeJees **raised** his eyes and **looked** at George and Paddy, but both **shook** their heads.   A→B and (A)→B, but A→B

186. It wasn't either of them.   A＝B

The voice **had come** from behind BeeJees.   A↻

p.57 "Uh-uh,"   不完全な文

Frank **said** again, smiling his toothless smile.   A↻

He **was** rolling around in his wagon.   A＝B

"What, Frank?" BeeJees **said**, a little annoyed.   A→B

187. Frank **gave** them all a big proud smile and **said**, "Eddie findie cat."   A→B／B' and (A)→B

They all **stared** at each other.   A→B

Frank **nodded** to himself as if he were sure.   A↻

Then he **looked** at Willy's stroller and **nodded** a second time.   A→B and (A)↻

With a great big smile, he **pointed** straight towards Old Everville and **repeated** in a confident voice.   A→B and (A)↻

"Ed always findie cat."   A→B

---

182. To hell with it! はやけくそになった時の決まり文句。「何もかも地獄へ行っちまえ!」という強烈な言い回しです。あえて書くならば、it は「今のこの状況」の代役。

183. yanked はつかんでいたものを勢いよくひっぱる時に用いられます。spun（spin）は「スピンする」で、キキーッと車体全体が大きく弧を描きながら曲がる様子を表現しています。drift は「漂う」という意味の矢印として登場することが多い言葉ですが、ここでは「(雪の)吹きだまり」という役者として使われています。crashing 以下は「どのように」の付録で、head first は「頭から先に」。

184. 前半は wind が old theater を「foundations（土台）から揺らした」と説明しています。how 以下が分かりにくい場合は、how dangerous outside was. に置き換えてください。

185. 肯定を表す Uh-huh（三色辞典 16 ページ参照）に対して、こちらは否定を表す Uh-uh です。

186. It は「Uh-uh と口にした someone」の代役。

187. フランクのセリフなので独特の言い方ですが、" " 内は正しくは Ed will find the cat.

ビッグ・ファット・キャットの三色辞典

The car had run off the road near the top of the hill.　A↩
It landed in a ditch, one tire buried deep in the snow.　A↩
The engine was still alive, but the headlights were both
　　smashed.　A＝B, but A＝B
Ed opened the back door of the limousine and stepped out into
　　the snow.　A→B and (A)↩
He had hit his head.　A→B
His right temple was bleeding a little.　A＝B
He peered inside the car to check if Jeremy was okay.　A→B

188.Jeremy seemed to be shaken-up, but he wasn't injured.
　　A＝B, but A＝B
Ed sighed with relief, but before Jeremy could recover enough
　　to stop him, he started walking down the hill, straight into
　　the snowstorm.　A↩, but A→B

The snow came up to his knees, and it was difficult to walk
　　even a few steps.　A↩, and A＝B
189.The wind threatened his balance and the blowing snow
　　suffocated him.　A→B and A→B
But he didn't stop.　A↩

190.He waded forward, digging through the snow, fighting his way
　　down the hill.　A↩
His whole body was so cold.　A＝B
His feet seemed like someone else's feet.　A＝B
Down below, he could see nothing but white, white, white land.
　　A→B
Snow had covered everything.　A→B
He remembered that the Outside Mall was at the bottom of the
　　hill, but all he could see was snow.　A→B, but A＝B
Even if the cat were somewhere down there, he had no idea
　　how to find it.　A→B
But he kept going anyway.　A→B

191.Halfway down the hill, his legs gave out and he fell forward,
　　tumbling down the hill, creating a long cloud of snow in the
　　air.　A↩ and A↩
192.He rolled all the way down, and finally stopped after sliding
　　another few feet across flat ground.　A↩, and (A)↩
He moaned in pain but got up.　A↩ but (A)↩
"Caaat!" Ed shouted into the blizzard, but the wind erased his
　　voice.　A→B, but A→B

p.58

188. shaken-up はシェイクされたあとのように茫然としている状態を指します。shockedほど大げさでない状況によく使われる言葉です。

189.「風がthreatened（おどす）した」と言うと妙なようですが、あえてそう表現することで強い風にバランスを失いそうなエドの様子を表現しています。

p.59

190. wade というのは本来浅い水の中などを歩く時に使いますが、雪やぬかるみの中をかき分けるように進む時にも使います。fighting his way は「道と戦う」で、歩きにくい道を苦労して進んでいくイメージです。

191. gave out（give out）は gave up（give up）とよく似ているのですが、前者は「力尽きる」、後者は「あきらめる」といったイメージのちがいがあります。

192. all the way は「すべての道」、転じて「はるばる」という意味の言葉ですが、rolled と down の間に入ることによって、かなり長い距離を「転がり落ちた」雰囲気を出しています。

p.60

Big Fat Cat's 3 Color Dictionary

p.60

He called out even louder, "Caaat! Where are you!? Caaaat!!"
  A→B

p.61

Only the wind answered.   A↩

Ed was too cold and too tired to think.   A=B

The snow was all around him.   A=B

193. It came from all directions, completely blinding him.   A↩

His hands were half-frozen and the cold had entered his lungs.
  A=B and A→B

194. He was losing his sense of direction.   A=B

He knew he was somewhere near the shop, but everything was hidden under the snow.   A→B, but A=B

195. The world was just one big white blur.   A=B

"Cat..."   不完全な文

Ed didn't know if he was standing or not.   A→B

196. He realized he had closed his eyes sometime before.   A→B

He was so tired.   A=B

"Cat... I'm sorry..."   不完全な文   A=B

Then, everything began to fade.   A→B

Everything became white with the snow.   A=B

193. It は snow の代役。

194. sense of direction で「方向感覚」。

195. ここでの world はエドの目から見た「世界」。

196. sometime「いつか」、before「以前の」で、「(現在より前の)どこかの時点で」目を閉じていたということ。

p.62

Willy?   不完全な文

p.64

"Son, you're going to freeze to death if you sleep here," Willy said with a smile.   A→B

Ed got to his knees, thinking vaguely, *you should put on this muffler, Willy.*   A↩

It's really cold today.   A=B

"Willy," Ed said.   A→B

"I'm sorry.   A=B

I... I was late again.   A=B

I'm always late."   A=B

Willy smiled.   A↩

"No, Ed."   不完全な文

Despite all the wind and snow, Willy's voice was clear and calm.
  A=B

197. It still had that warm tone.   A→B

"You were never late.   A=B

198. You've always made it just in time.   A→B

199. You found that cat just before it starved to death.   A→B

You learned a great lesson just before you gave up.   A→B

You found the real meaning of winning just before you won...
  A→B

197. It は Willy's voice の代役。

198. 「時間以内に」を示す in time は、いつも遅れてばかりいたエドにとって、あこがれの言葉なのかもしれません。

199. starved to death は「死ぬまで飢える」で「飢え死にする」。

ビッグ・ファット・キャットの三色辞典

And you saved my soul... all, just in time."   A→B   p.64
Ed shook his head.   A→B

"No. I... I... Willy... I've lost my cat...   不完全な文   A→B   p.65
I went after him, but I was late again.   A↩, but A=B
He saved me.   A→B
He was always there with me and I was late..."   A=B and A=B
Willy just stood there smiling.   A↩
"No, Ed. I told you.   不完全な文   A→B
You were always there in time.   A=B
200. You just didn't see it that way."   A→B
"But Willy... I... I..."   不完全な文
The moon somehow appeared in the sky through the snow.   A↩
It was the same moon as the one they had seen on the way to
    the hospital.   A=B
It was still beautiful.   A=B
Willy smiled one final time.   A↩
"You've always made it in time... and you made it just in time
    again," said Willy.   A→B
"Now wake up."   (A)↩

200. it は今までエドが遅れたと思ってきた状況すべての代役。that way は前文の You were always there in time. を受けて「(いつも間に合ったという)方向で」。

"Willy...?"   不完全な文   p.66
Ed opened his eyes halfway and realized he had fainted
    somewhere in the snow.   A→B and (A)→B
He was barely able to get to his knees.   A=B
He looked around for Willy, but there was nothing but the
    snowstorm around him.   A→B, but A=B
"Willy... I..."   不完全な文
Ed stopped, noticing that he was holding something in his right
    hand beneath the snow.   A↩
He pulled his hand out and a string came out from under the
    snow.   A→B and A↩
201. He didn't realize what it was for a moment.   A→B
202. He just stared at it.   A→B
But slowly, very slowly, he realized that he had seen the string
    before.   A→B
He pulled the string from under the snow.   A→B
203. A ragged gingerbread man was connected to it.   A=B
Ed opened his eyes wider and pulled on the string frantically.
    A→B and (A)↩
A line of gingerbread man decorations popped out of the snow
    in front of him.   A↩

201. it は前文の string の代役。

202. この it も string の代役。

203. gingerbread man は『Big Fat Cat and the Mustard Pie』でも紹介した、ジンジャー(しょうが)の粉末の入った人形型のクッキーですが、ここで登場する gingerbread man はプラスチック製の飾りです。

- 30 -

p.66
204. It was a decoration from Pie Heaven's front window. A = B
Ed got to his feet. A ↩
The storm seemed to have weakened a little. A = B
205. Ed quickly tugged on the line. A ↩
206. The other end was stuck under a snow-covered box a few feet away. A = B

p.67
Ed rushed over to the box and wiped the snow off the top of the box. A ↩ and (A) → B
207. It was his old glass showcase. A = B
Ed used his hands to find the edge of the case. A → B
This was the showcase he had always stored his blueberry pies in. A = B
He pulled off the top of the case and looked inside. A → B and (A) → B
The snow had penetrated the case, filling up half of its interior. A → B
Ed dug the snow out with both hands, ignoring the pain in his fingertips. A → B
He finally managed to get most of the snow out. A → B
"No..." Ed gasped. A → B
Buried under the snow, in a corner of the case, was a ball of fur. A = B
"Oh no..." 不完全な文
The ball of fur didn't move. A ↩
Ed knelt down on the snow with trembling hands. A ↩
"Cat..." Ed said. A → B
208. The tears he had held back came now. A ↩
He said in a weak voice, "Cat... wake up... please." A → B

p.68
Ed reached out and touched the body of the cat. A ↩ and (A) → B
It was cold. A = B
Ed gulped. A ↩
209. A shiver ran down his spine. A ↩
210. "Cat... come on. 不完全な文 (A) ↩
I found you. A → B
I found you again. A → B
This time, I know I'm not late. A → B
Now wake up!" (A) ↩
From the day it had come into Pie Heaven, it had always been his cat. A = B
It had preferred his blueberry pies right from the start. A → B

---

204. ありし日の gingerbread man は『Big Fat Cat and the Mustard Pie』12～13ページの挿絵でご覧ください。

205. ひも状の何かをたぐりよせる動作が tugged です。釣り竿を引く時や、綱引きの綱を引っ張る時に使われることが多い単語です。line は gingerbread man をつないでいる string のこと。

206. エドが持っている部分からつながっている line の、「もう一方の端」が The other end です。

207. It は the box の代役。

208. この held には back がついているので「(つかんで)押し戻す」というニュアンスがあります。

209. 日本語でも「背筋が寒くなる」という表現がありますが、同じ内容を英語ではこう表します。

210. come on も大変よく使われる言い回しで、「on(点灯している状態)になれ!」と言うことで誰かを励ましたり、その気にさせたりする時に使います。

It was his one and only cat.　A = B

"You can't sleep here, cat!　A↩

C'mon, I wasn't late, damn it!　(A) ↩, A = B

211. I swear I wasn't late this time!"　A → B

There was no answer.　A = B

The cat lay perfectly still.　A↩

But somehow, Ed knew the cat could hear him.　A → B

The cat had always come back to him, and it would come back, one final time.　A↩, and A↩

"C'mon!　(A) ↩

I'll bake you all the blueberry pies you want.　A → B／B'

Just... just wake up. Please.　(A) ↩　不完全な文

CAT! WAKE UP!"　不完全な文　(A) ↩

But still, no response. No response at all.　不完全な文　不完全な文

212. All strength began to run out of Ed.　A → B

He stood there a while staring at the motionless body of the cat.
　　A↩

It seemed so cold lying there in the snow.　A = B

Ed took off his muffler and covered the cat.　A → B and (A) → B

He bent down and picked the cat up, wrapping it inside the muffler.　A↩ and (A) → B

The cat's body was still slightly warm.　A = B

And heavy.　不完全な文

213. He realized this was the first time he had ever held the cat and it made him cry.　A → B and A → B = B'

"I'm sorry...　A = B

I forgot... for a moment there in the mall, I forgot... and you... you probably thought I... I'm sorry, cat."
　　A↩, A↩ and A → B... A = B

The cat moved.　A↩

214. Ed thought he had imagined it, but the cat slowly looked up at him with a big frown.　A → B, but A → B

"Cat?"　不完全な文

The cat was looking around for blueberry pie and found none.
　　A = B and (A) → B

215. In a very frustrated mood, it glared at Ed for waking it up during a perfectly good nap.　A → B

It sneezed once and swiftly jumped out of Ed's hands.
　　A↩ and (A) ↩

Ed was completely frozen for a moment.　A = B

He stared at the cat with disbelief.　A → B

p.68

211. 差し迫った状況でよく登場するのがこの「I swear ○○」という言い回しです。「絶対に○○だ!」ということを伝えたいけれども、「I promise ○○」では少し弱い場合に、この表現が出てきます。ただし、あまり上品な言い方ではないので、うかつに使うことはお勧めできません。

212. strength は「強さ」や「力」を示す意味の言葉ですが、power が主に肉体的な「力」を指すのに対して、strength は精神的な「力」も含んだ「強さ」を表現する場合に使います。

p.69

213. it は前半の文の内容の代役です。

214. it は前文全体の代役。

215. 最初の In からカンマまでは it (the cat) につく付録です。for 以下は「なぜ猫が Ed に glared したか」の説明になっています。

p.69

216. **The cat was** taking a stretch as if nothing had happened. A = B
"Cat...? You're... *okay*?" 不完全な文 A = B
The cat yawned. A ↩
Ed reached out for the cat, but **the cat**, as always, **scratched** him.
　　A→B, but A→B
"You're okay?!" Ed **said**. A→B
"Oh my God. You're okay!" 不完全な文 A = B
Ed closed his eyes tightly as great relief rushed through him.
　　A→B
It was a moment so unbelievable that he couldn't even breathe for a few seconds. A = B
He opened his eyes again and **looked** at the cat.
　　A→B and (A)→B
The cat was still staring at him. A = B

217. "I come all this way to find you, and you're taking a nap, you damn thing," **Ed said** with a smile on his face, tears in his eyes and snow in his hair. A→B

p.70

As Ed wiped his eyes, **he realized** that the snow and wind were beginning to calm down. A→B

218. **Only** a gentle shower of snowflakes **was** now falling from the sky. A = B

219. "Cat... all during the time I was searching for you, I was thinking why I needed you so much. And I think I finally know now," **Ed said** as he knelt down in front of the cat. A→B
A beautiful white world enveloped them as they sat there together in the ruins of Pie Heaven. A→B
"Mom **gave** me the recipe, Willy **gave** me the courage... but you..." A→B／B', A→B／B' 不完全な文
Ed paused. A ↩
"You **gave** me the reason. A→B／B'
Even when nobody came to my shop, **you were** always there to eat my pies. A = B

220. ***You* were** the one that made me a baker. A = B

221. **I would have quit** baking a long time ago if it wasn't for you."
　　A→B
Ed smiled and **said** to the cat in a voice that was his most sincere, "Thanks. Thanks a lot." A ↩ and (A)→B

p.71

For a moment, **time itself seemed** to pause. A = B

222. **The world was** quiet and forgiving in the silent snowfall. A = B

---

216. taking a stretch は「ストレッチする」で、猫がよく行っている体を伸ばす動作を指します。

217. you damn thing は本来は怒っている時の言い方ですが、ここでは猫が生きていたうれしさに、思わずエドが口にした「愛すべき悪口」になっています。この雪の中で生き延びた猫を見た直後ですから、thing という表現を使って猫を「物」か「化け物」扱いするのも無理はないかもしれません。

218. snow には積もっている「雪」や、天気としての「雪」のイメージがありますが、snowflakes は美しい結晶の形をした、一粒一粒の「雪」のイメージです。空から降る雪が、今までのような嵐ではなく、穏やかな粉雪に変わったことを指しています。

219. セリフ内を色分けすると、all during the time I was searching for you, I was thinking why I needed you so much. And I think I finally know now.
A = B   A → B

220. You made me a baker. の You (= cat) をさらに強調した言い方です。

Even then, **Ed knew** in the back of his mind, **that time would start moving** again soon.   A→B

He would have to apologize to a lot of people, and **he would also have to find** a way to build a new life.   A→B and A→B

But for now, **he didn't care**.   A↩

It was only him and the cat — just as it was in the beginning.   A=B

Ed stood up.   A↩

You are a baker, Ed.   A=B

Just a baker without a shop.   不完全な文

Now go back. Bake your pie.   (A)↩ (A)→B

"**I will,** Willy," **Ed whispered** to himself as he wrapped the muffler around him.   A→B

The cat had become tired of waiting.   A=B

It decided to scratch Ed again.   A→B

"**I know, I know.**   A↩, A↩

I'll bake you a blueberry pie as soon as we get home.   A→B／B'

223. **I have to get** the Magic Pie Shop ready anyway."   A→B

The cat scratched him for an answer.   A→B

Ed smiled.   A↩

"And cat, **you really need** a name," he said.   A→B

The snowstorm had reduced all the colors in the world to a big white land of snow.   A→B

In the distance, **a police siren was coming** their way.   A=B

Ed and the cat started walking back towards town, their footsteps lined close together in the snow.   A→B

This night will end, but soon, **a new day will begin** in the town of Everville.   A↩, but A↩

There are a lot of pies in this world.   A=B

Some are sweeter than others.   A=B

Some are sour.   A=B

Some are even spicy or bitter or hot.   A=B

But that's not important.   A=B

What's important is that every pie is different.   A=B

Every pie has its own taste.   A→B

My pie may not be sweet — it may seem funny at first sight.
   A=B A=B

---

p.71

221. quit baking は「(パイを) 焼くのをやめる」こと。if 以下はその理由を指していて「(お前のためでなかったら) パイを焼くのをやめていただろう」という文になります。難しいフレーズですが、無理に正確な意味をとろうとせず、前後からの流れで読む感覚を大事にしてください。if 以下を if you weren't there に置き換えてもかまいません。

222. snow が「積もった雪」、snowflake が「雪の結晶」だとすると、snowfall は「降ってくる雪」です。言葉自体にも少し離れた場所から一面に降る雪を見ているようなイメージがあります。

223. get ○○ ready は「○○の ready な状態」を get すると書いて「準備をする」。

p.72

p.74

p.76

p.77

p.78

p.79　But *it's all I have*, and *it's all mine*.　A＝B, and A＝B
And whatever the pie... whatever the taste... if you have friends, family, and of course... a cat you love... that pie will always taste good.　A↩

p.80　*Even if it is... a mustard pie.*　不完全な文

ビッグ・ファット・キャットの三色辞典
〜雪の夜編〜

三色辞典の使い方

赤い色は **A** の箱
緑の色は→、↩または＝
青い色は **B** の箱
濃い青色は二つ目の **B'** の箱
（めったにありませんが）
色がないのは付録
そして、これが文の形

Ed gave the cat a present yesterday.　A→B／B'

分かりにくい文については、ページの右側に少し詳しい解説が載っています。同じ数字のついた文と照らし合わせてご覧ください。

この三色辞典は『ビッグ・ファット・キャットの世界一簡単な英語の本』で紹介されている方法論に基づき、本編の英文を色分けして、解説を加えたヒントブックです。もちろん「答え」ではありません。考える上でのひとつのガイドラインとしてお使いください。